An illustrated history of

FIREARMS

by Ian V. Hogg

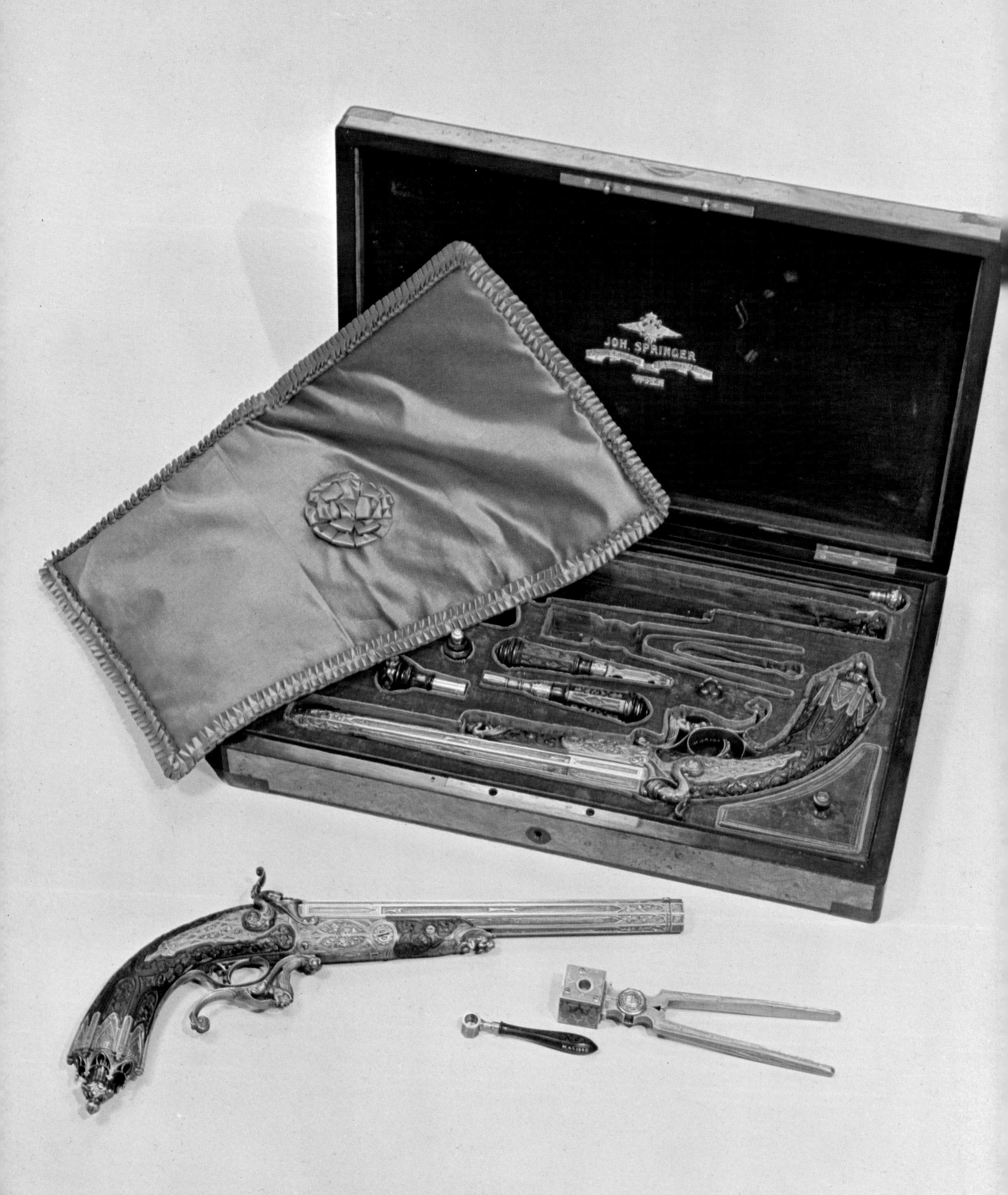
JOH. SPRINGER

An illustrated history of

FIREARMS

by Ian V. Hogg

A QUARTO BOOK

Published in the United States of America
in 1981 by A & W Publishers, Inc.
95 Madison Avenue
New York, New York 10016
By arrangement with Quarto Publishing Limited

ISBN 0 88365 484 9

This book was designed and produced by Quarto Publishing Limited, 32 Kingly Court, London W1

Colour separation by Sakai Lithocolour Company Limited, Hong Kong
Printed by Leefung-Asco Printers Limited, Hong Kong

Endpapers
An international shooting competition between America and Ireland, 1875

Frontispiece
An elaborate example of a cased pair of pistols with matching accessories. They are breech-loading centre-fire target pistols with ebony stocks fitted with mounts of chiselled iron in the Gothic style. Austrian (Vienna), about 1860.

CONTENTS

FOREWORD

ALTHOUGH THE FIREARM has a long history, as the introductory section of this book outlines, the amount of technical progress during the first five hundred years was relatively small. Apart from the flintlock mechanism, there was little in a musket of 1800 which would have puzzled an arquebusier of 1400 had he lived to see one. But the opening years of the 19th century saw two significant advances: the adoption of the percussion principle and of rifling, and these began a revolution in weapons design. Ignition of the propellant became certain and instantaneous, and the flight of the bullet became accurate. Within a comparatively few years the revolver had taken shape, the bolt-action breech-loading rifle had been devised, and the metallic self-contained cartridge appeared. There has been more technical advance in the last 150 years than had taken place in the previous five hundred or so.

In order to keep this book to a manageable size, some decisions had to be taken about the scope of its contents, and the primary decision was of a date at which to begin our survey. After much discussion, we have selected 1830. Forsyth's percussion principle had been patented and was entering common use; percussion caps had appeared; Dreyse was working on his bolt-action Needle Gun and Lefaucheaux was developing the pinfire cartridge. From 1830 onward, the inventions and designs, stimulated by the inventive awareness of the 19th century and aided by the rapid improvements in machinery and manufacturing technique due to the Industrial Revolution, became an ever-widening stream.

Into this stream we have cast a very selective line; the sheer number of firearms designs patented since 1830 would fill several volumes, and we have, therefore, chosen those which we think deserve mention for their innovation, their effect on firearms history and design, their wide use in war and recreation, and their outright fame. It might be thought that there is a bias toward military weapons rather than sporting ones, but the fact, unpalatable as it may be, remains that the far greater part of firearms development has its roots in military requirements, and it is after the military application has been seen to work that the idea then passes to the sporting side. In other hands, the mixture and balance might well have been different; but we believe that the following pages offer the reader the significant elements of the history of firearms in a convenient and concise form.

IAN V. HOGG

THE HAND GONNE

c.1350

Illustration from a manuscript c.1400, showing a hand gonne being ignited by a hot iron.

THE EARLY HISTORY of firearms is, of course, allied with that of gunpowder, and it is a matter for regret among students and researchers that no-one in the Middle Ages appears to have been sufficiently impressed by either one to have made some reliable record of their first appearance. As a result, speculation has run rife, and it is only in the present century that most of the legend and conjecture has been exposed to detailed scrutiny and swept away, to be replaced by more reasoned conclusions.

In the past, the invention of gunpowder has been ascribed to such very varied sources as the Chinese, the Greeks, the Arabs and the Hindus, but none of these claims will withstand critical testing. One remarkable thing is that while each of these races has records and artifacts reaching back well before the period of interest to us, none can produce valid evidence of a knowledge of gunpowder or firearms any earlier than can be proved in Western Europe. Certainly the Greeks had 'Greek Fire' and the Chinese employed various pyrotechnic substances, but neither of these were gunpowder nor did they possess explosive properties: to argue otherwise is like asserting that automobiles must have existed in 1880 because there are records of bicycles at that date.

The first undisputed records of the existence of gunpowder occur in the writings of Roger Bacon, a Franciscan Friar of Ilchester; in about 1260 he buried the formula in an anagram, while in essays written in 1267–8 he referred to it openly as 'the powder, known in divers places, composed of saltpetre, sulphur and charcoal.' From that time on, records became more numerous and gunpowder (or black powder), though an expensive commodity, became more common.

But the question now arises: to what purpose was it put? Bacon refers to it being wrapped in parchment and ignited to give a 'blinding flash and stunning noise', and it seems probable that the earliest days saw it used principally as a novelty. How, and when, and by whom the ability to use it to propel a missile was discovered is not known with any certainty. For years the legend of 'Black Berthold', the mysterious monk of Freiburg, held sway; that one day he was preparing gunpowder in an apothecary's mortar when the mixture ignited and blew the pestle from the mortar.

From this, the story ran, he deduced the use of gunpowder in a closed vessel and invented the gun, and the use of the word 'mortar' for a particular piece of ordnance commemorates this occasion. Unfortunately, no two authorities seem to have agreed on when Berthold performed this vital experiment, and the earliest date ascribed to it is a good deal later than that of definite and proveable records of cannon. Moreover, the term 'mortar' was not to appear for many years, and recent researchers have suggested that Berthold never existed at all but was pure legend from start to finish.

The earliest incontestable record of a firearm is the famous 'Millimete Cannon', so-called from being depicted in a manuscript by Walter de Millimete of England and dated 1326. In the same year there is reference in the records of Florence to the provision of guns and shot for defending the town. It would thus seem that by 1326 the cannon was known across Europe and, by inference, must have been known for some time to allow such distribution to take place. The principal difficulty in identifying the early use of firearms is the haphazard use of the word 'artillery' interchangeably between mechanical engines—catapults, ballistae and mangonels—and firearms: since the one usurped the function of the other, it adopted the same generic term, and in the early

Hand gonnes accompanying full-sized cannon and archers in a 15th century siege. Explosive ordnance development was under way.

records of battles and sieges it is often almost impossible to say which of the two distinct types of 'artillery' were in use.

In the 1350s, though, we begin to see references to 'gunnis cum telar'—guns with handles—marking the emergence of the personal firearm. In the normal course of events we might reasonably expect that a new device would begin small and become larger as experience was gained, but with the firearm this natural order of things is reversed. The first firearms were cannon, albeit small cannon, and from this beginning design moved in two directions, upwards to make bigger and more powerful cannon, and downwards to make 'hand gonnes'.

Few weapons of this early period have survived; one of the best-known is that excavated from a well in Tannenburg Castle, and this weapon can be dated fairly accurately since it is known that the castle was razed in 1399. A similar weapon is the small bronze piece found at Loshult, Sweden, in 1861 and estimated to date from the early years of the 14th century. Other examples have been excavated in Germany and Central Europe, and as a result these early hand gonnes can be seen to have several points of similarity. In general, they appear to have consisted of a wooden stave some three feet long to which a cast bronze or iron barrel was fixed by iron bands. The barrel varied in length from one to three feet, and the smooth bore was from a half to one-and-a-half inches in calibre. In some instances the barrel appears to have been cast as an open-ended tube, a plug being driven into the rear end in order to seal it. A vent, or touch-hole, was drilled through the metal at the rear end of the bore.

To fire, the hand gonne was charged with a quantity of powder and a ball or a handful of stones or small shot. Powder was then sprinkled in the vent, and the weapon grasped by its stave, tuck-

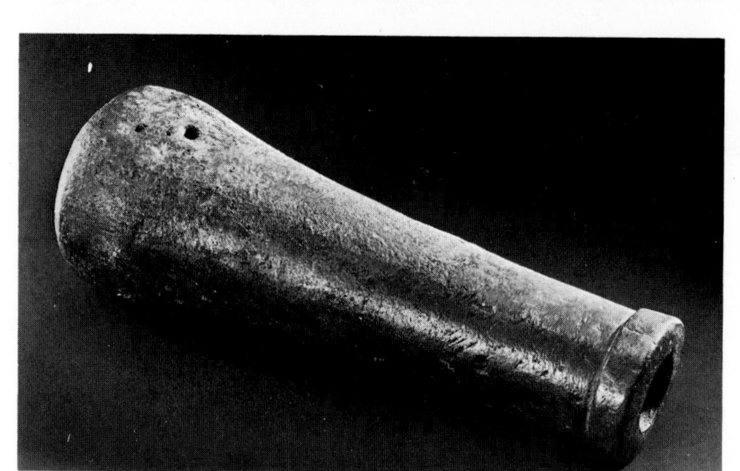

Above **Two Swiss hand guns of the 14th century, one fitted with a recoil hook to become a 'hakenbuchse'.**

Left **A 14th century bronze hand gun from Loshult, Sweden.**

GUNPOWDER

Gunpowder is an intimate mixture of saltpetre, charcoal and sulphur: the earliest formula, that of Roger Bacon, gives the proportions as 7:5:5, or 41% saltpetre, 29½% charcoal and 29½% sulphur. This gradually changed, the percentage of saltpetre increasing, until by the end of the 18th century it had reached its final form: 75% saltpetre, 15% charcoal and 10% sulphur.

The earliest powder was called 'serpentine' and was a finely ground powder. This had certain defects: packed tightly in a gun chamber it was difficult to ignite and slow to burn, and in storage and transport had a distinct tendency to separate out into its constituent parts. During the 15th century the French invented 'corned' powder, in which the three substances were mixed together in the wet state (which was a much safer method than dry mixing) and the resulting paste dried. This was then crumbled and passed through sieves to produce granular powder. Such powder was more efficient in the gun, since the interstices between the grains allowed faster ignition and combustion, and since each grain was a solid compound the individual substances could not separate out. Early woodcuts show various stages in the making of powder: chopping the charcoal, wet-mixing the powder, breaking up the 'press-cake' and sieving the grains.

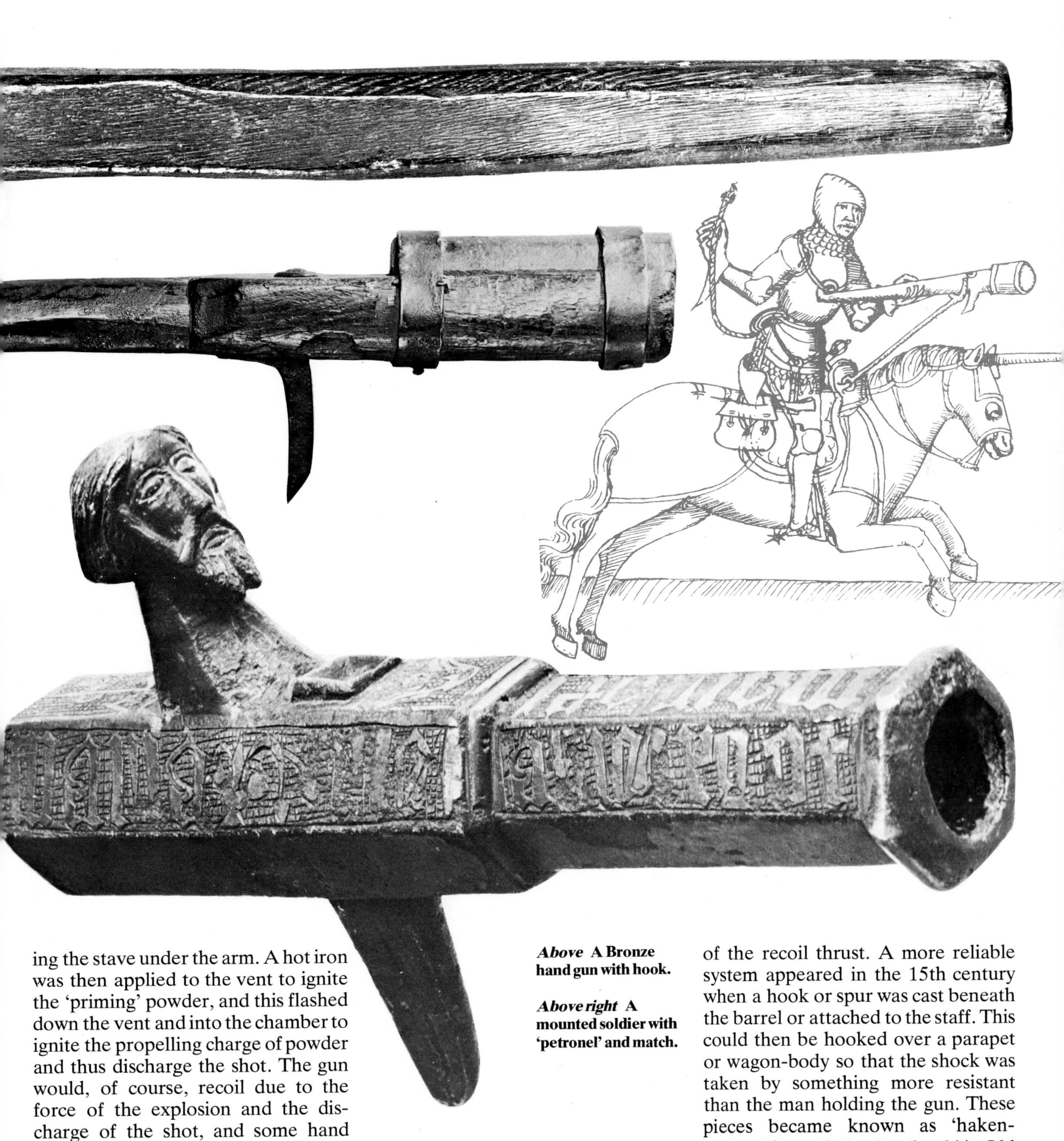

ing the stave under the arm. A hot iron was then applied to the vent to ignite the 'priming' powder, and this flashed down the vent and into the chamber to ignite the propelling charge of powder and thus discharge the shot. The gun would, of course, recoil due to the force of the explosion and the discharge of the shot, and some hand gonnes have been found with the end of the staff formed into a knob or ball, which, it is suggested, might have been rested on the ground to absorb some

Above **A Bronze hand gun with hook.**

Above right **A mounted soldier with 'petronel' and match.**

of the recoil thrust. A more reliable system appeared in the 15th century when a hook or spur was cast beneath the barrel or attached to the staff. This could then be hooked over a parapet or wagon-body so that the shock was taken by something more resistant than the man holding the gun. These pieces became known as 'hakenbuchse' (from 'haken' = 'hook' in Old German) and this, in turn, was gradually corrupted to 'harquebus' or 'arquebus'.

THE MATCHLOCK

15th CENTURY

THE MOST INCONVENIENT thing about the early hand gonnes was the awkward system of ignition by hot iron; obviously a hand-gunner could not stray far from the brazier in which he heated his iron. For defensive purposes this was no great drawback, since braziers were placed on the ramparts of a castle or defensive work, but for field use the method was impractical. Some time towards the end of the 14th century the matter was resolved by the invention of 'slow match'. This consisted of loosely woven hemp cord boiled in a solution of saltpetre and then allowed to dry. Due to the impregnation, when ignited the cord would smoulder slowly and reliably, always presenting a brightly burning end which could be used to ignite gunpowder. A hank of slow match could be carried more easily than a hot iron and, once ignited, could be carried for several hours, looped loosely in the fingers, so that the foot soldier now had a convenient form of ignition with which he could roam far and wide about the battlefield. He had to take care of it, though; Cyprian Lucar, an English gunner writing in 1588, observed that 'A Gunner . . . ought not, for any prayers or reward, lend any piece of his gunmatch to any other person, because it may be hurtful to him in time of service to lack the same. . .'

Even so, a hank of smouldering string was an inconvenient thing to be burdened with in the heat of battle; as with the hot iron, it still demanded the use of one hand and arm, which could not, therefore, be used to support the gun. Another point was that the gunner had to keep his eye on the gun so as to bring the match to the vent; if he kept his eyes on the target he might well miss the vent and plant the burning match on his wrist or fingers. Early in the 15th century these difficulties were ended by the invention of the matchlock. The earliest illustrated record is dated 1411 and shows a hand gonne with wooden staff, on which is mounted a long Z-shaped arm. At the

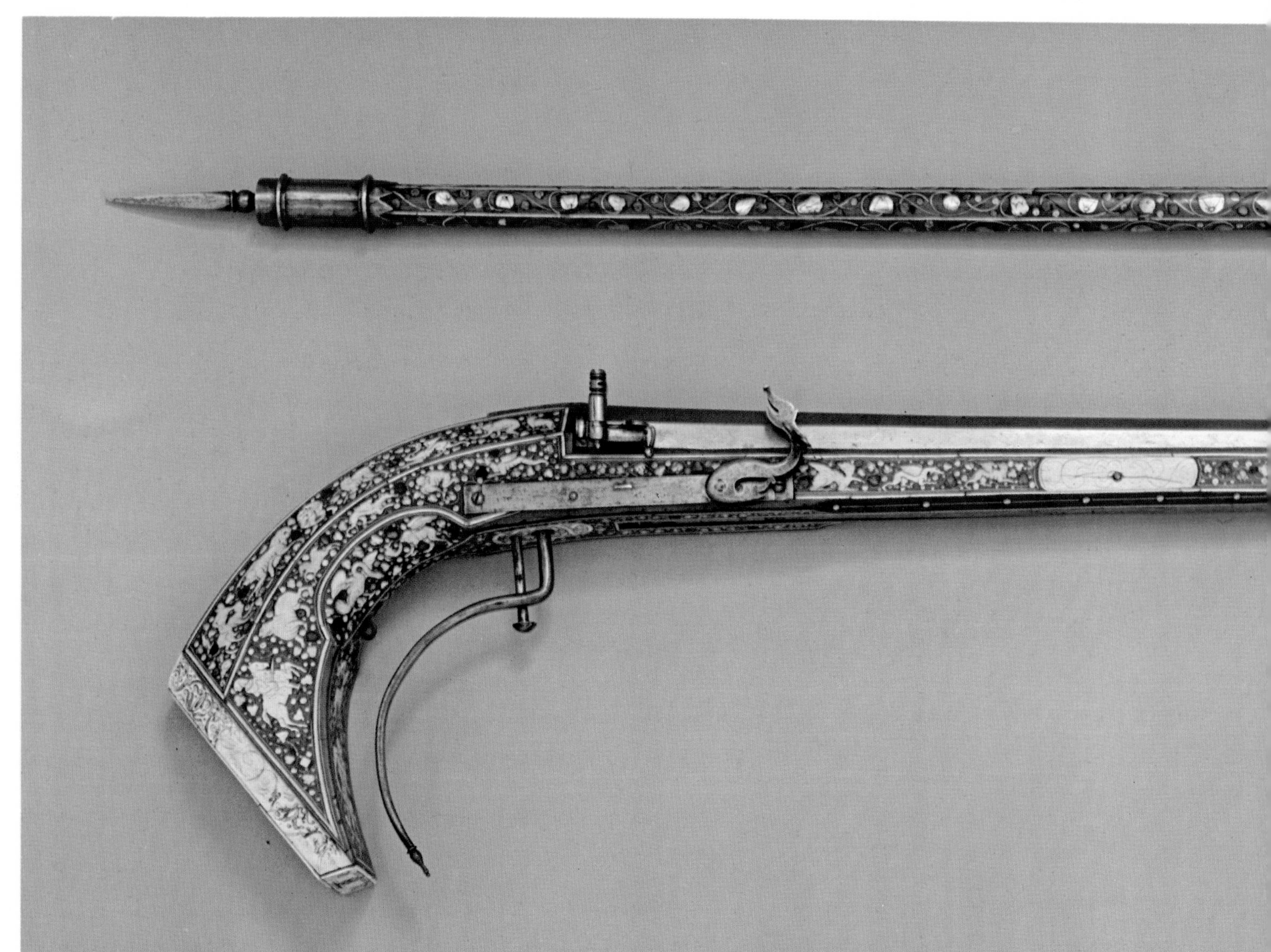

forward end of this arm is a piece of burning slowmatch, and this is being forced down into contact with the vent by the gunner pulling up on the other end, the Z being pivoted to the staff in its centre.

This was cumbersome, but it soon inspired improvement. As it happened, the contemporary crossbow used a similar Z-shaped catch to retain the bowstring and release it, and this was adapted to become the 'match lock'. The operation was the same but the device was more compact. In the first models the stock of the gun was slotted to allow the 'serpentine' (the Z-shaped piece) to pass through, and a pivot pin held it in place. The section above the stock held the match, while the section below acted as the trigger, being pulled back to bring the match to the vent. In a very short time the gunsmiths simplified construction by placing the vent in the side of the gun and surrounding its outer end with a 'pan', a saucer-like depression into which the priming powder was placed. This allowed the serpentine to be attached to the side of the stock, doing away with the need to cut slots in the woodwork. Then the whole affair, serpentine and pan, became a self-contained unit 'lock', attached to the 'lock plate' which was in turn attached to the side of the weapon.

Further detail improvement followed. A cover was placed on the pan; this could be slid forward to permit the priming to be loaded, then back to protect the powder from rain or spillage. When the time came to fire, the cover was opened again in order to allow contact of the burning match; when the cover was in place it was also a safeguard against sparks from the match inadvertently firing the gun before the firer was ready. More rapid action was achieved by the development of the 'snapping matchlock' in

An English musket rest of about 1630, the wooden shaft inlaid with mother-of-pearl and engraved staghorn. Below it a French matchlock of about 1575, the walnut stock inlaid with engraved and stained staghorn.

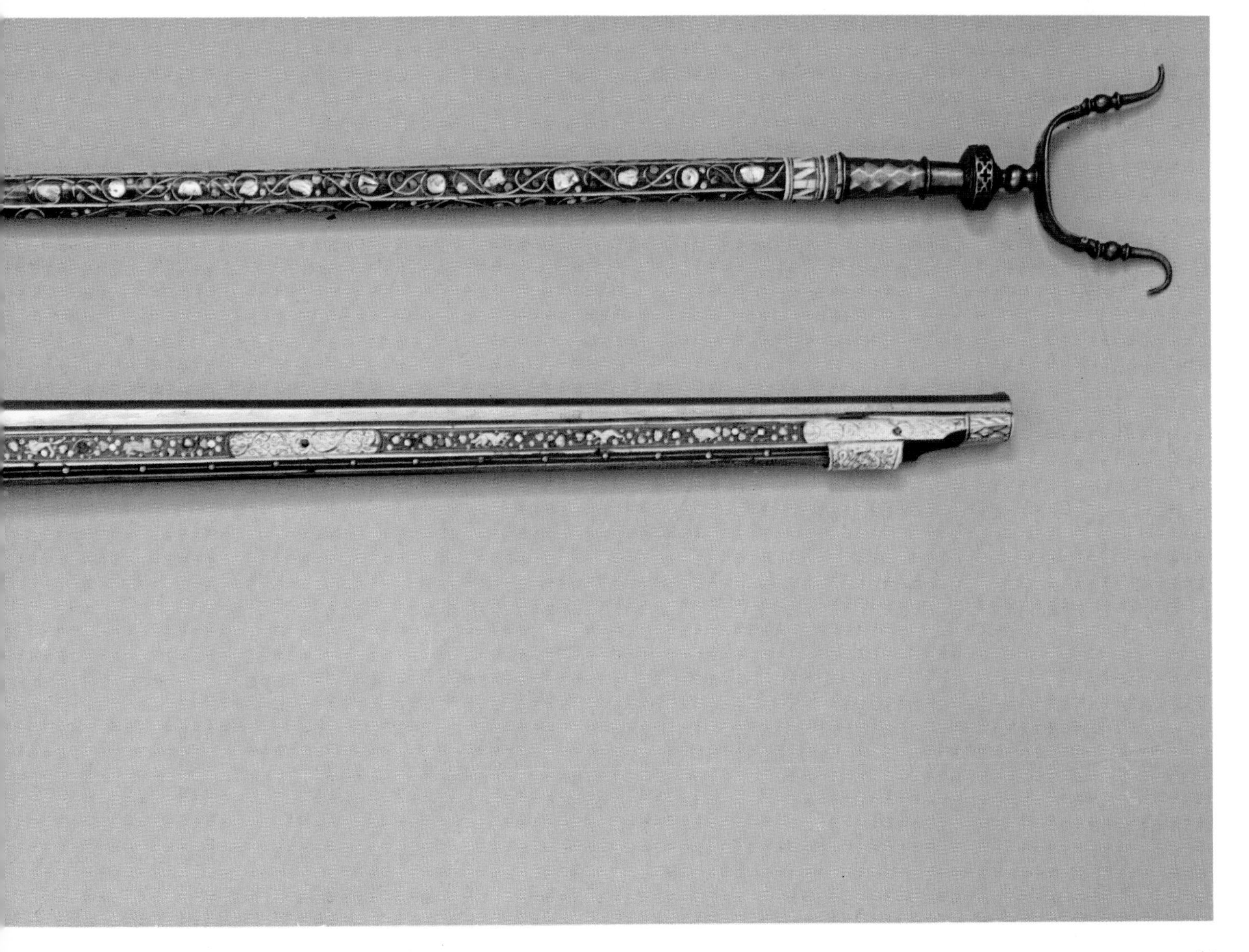

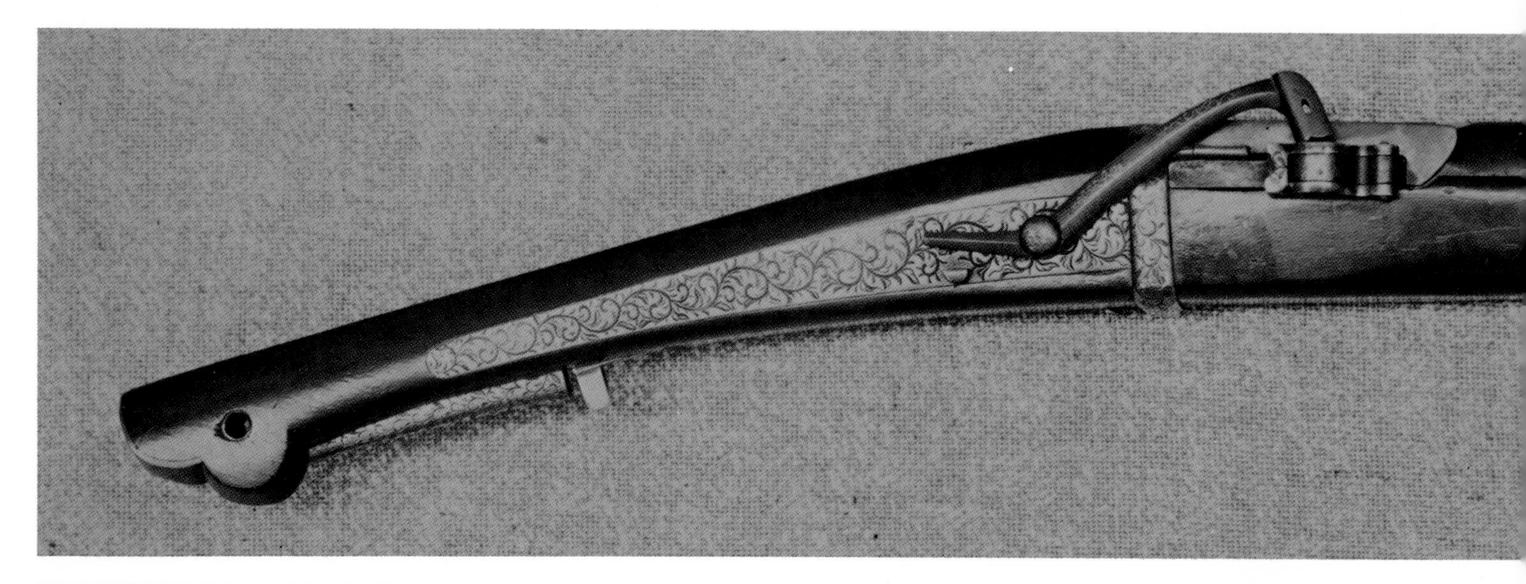

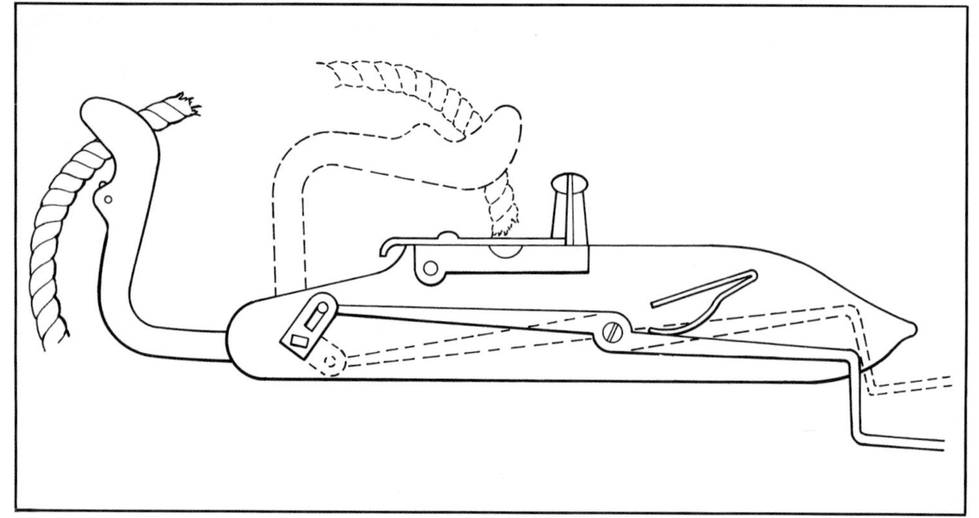

Top **A Japanese 18th century matchlock musket with inset silver decoration.**

Above right **An Arquebusier takes aim; notice the 'cartouches' slung around his waist, each containing one charge of bullet and powder.**

Above **The basic matchlock mechanism.**

Far right **A breech-loading matchlock shield-pistol belonging to Henry VIII.**

Right **Figure with matchlock, from a manuscript dated 1411.**

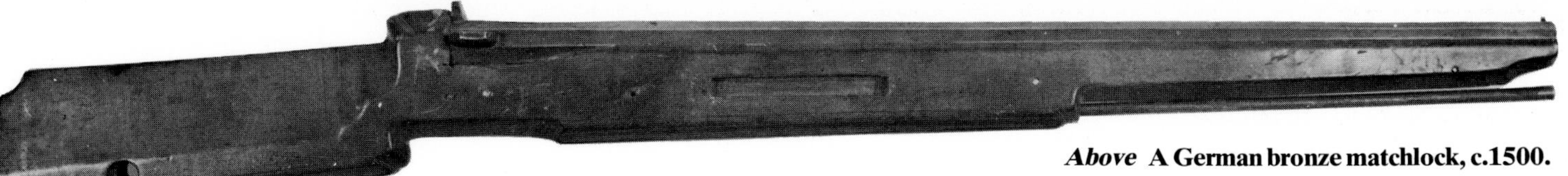

Above **A German bronze matchlock, c.1500.**

Below **An early matchlock, from an imaginatively illustrated manuscript of 1468.**

Loading a matchlock; a 16th century woodcut showing the way in which the hand-gonne's shaft had become shaped into a shoulder stock.

which the simple serpentine arm was replaced by a curved match-holder driven by a spring; the holder was drawn back and held by a trigger which, when pulled, released the holder to fly forward under pressure of the spring and carry the match into the pan. This type of matchlock, though soon superseded in Europe, was to remain in wide use in Japan until the 19th century. It had been taken there by Portuguese traders in the 16th century shortly before Japan cut herself off from the world, and since subsequent developments in firearms did not reach Japan, the snapping matchlock remained their normal ignition system far beyond its obsolescence in Europe.

The matchlock conferred benefits in other directions; now that the firer had no need to watch the match and vent to secure ignition, he could make some attempt at pointing the gun in the direction of the enemy more accurately. The stock of the weapon therefore changed from the round staff to a more flattened form which could be placed against the shoulder, one hand gripping the butt and operating the trigger while the other hand supported the barrel. Illustrations from the last quarter of the 15th century show this type of 'freehand' operation of matchlocks, but as a general rule the forked rest was still in wide use, principally because of the weight of the weapons. Arquebusses could weigh up to 20 lbs or more, and holding such a mass at the shoulder was not easy. 'Muskets' were somewhat lighter — about 15 lbs — and were easier to hold.

THE WHEEL-LOCK

16th CENTURY

WHILE THE MATCHLOCK was a moderately effective method of ignition, it still left a lot to be desired. One drawback was that if it chanced to rain, inevitably the match was extinguished and the army's firepower immediately fell to zero. Another tactical defect was that when a sentry was walking up and down at night, his movements were announced to the enemy by the glowing match, so that evading him became a very easy matter. But when it came to equipping armies, the matchlock had the supreme virtue of cheapness and simplicity; there was little involved in it, and even less in keeping it working in the field. And because of these advantages it stayed the standard infantry weapon for some two hundred years.

But there was an understandable desire on the part of gunsmiths to produce something more elegant, and in the opening years of the 16th century the wheel-lock was developed, probably in Germany. The origin of this mechanism is as indefinite as the origin of the gun itself: some authorities offer Leonardo da Vinci as the inventor on the strength of certain drawings which, though undated, have been reliably assessed as being from about 1508. These undoubtedly show a type of wheel-lock mechanism, but the concensus is that the device in question was a tinder igniter; an attempt to manufacture a gun lock to da Vinci's specification did not result in a working device. Another school of thought ascribes the invention to one Johann Kuhfuss or Kiefuss, a clockmaker of Nuremberg, and it certainly seems more likely that it originated with a clockmaker than with a gunsmith. But whoever was responsible, there are sufficient records to show that it was in use by 1510.

The wheel-lock mechanism is perpetuated in the cigarette lighter of today (or, rather, yesterday, since the arrival of the piezo-electric crystal)—a serrated wheel which is revolved rapidly in contact with a pyrophoric stone so that burning particles are thrown off. In the cigarette lighter the sparks strike a wick or a stream of gas; in the gun they were directed into the pan where they ignited the priming. The necessary impetus to the wheel was provided by a spring connected to the wheel's axle by a short length of chain. The axle had a square end on to which a 'spanner' could be placed and the wheel wound back so as to put the spring under tension. A locking pin then held the wheel against the spring's pull. When ready to fire the 'cock' was thrown forward; this was a hinged arm carrying a piece of iron pyrites in a jaw, so that the pyrites was held firmly against the wheel surface alongside the powder-charged pan. Pulling the trigger now released the wheel, striking off sparks from the pyrites and igniting the gunpowder.

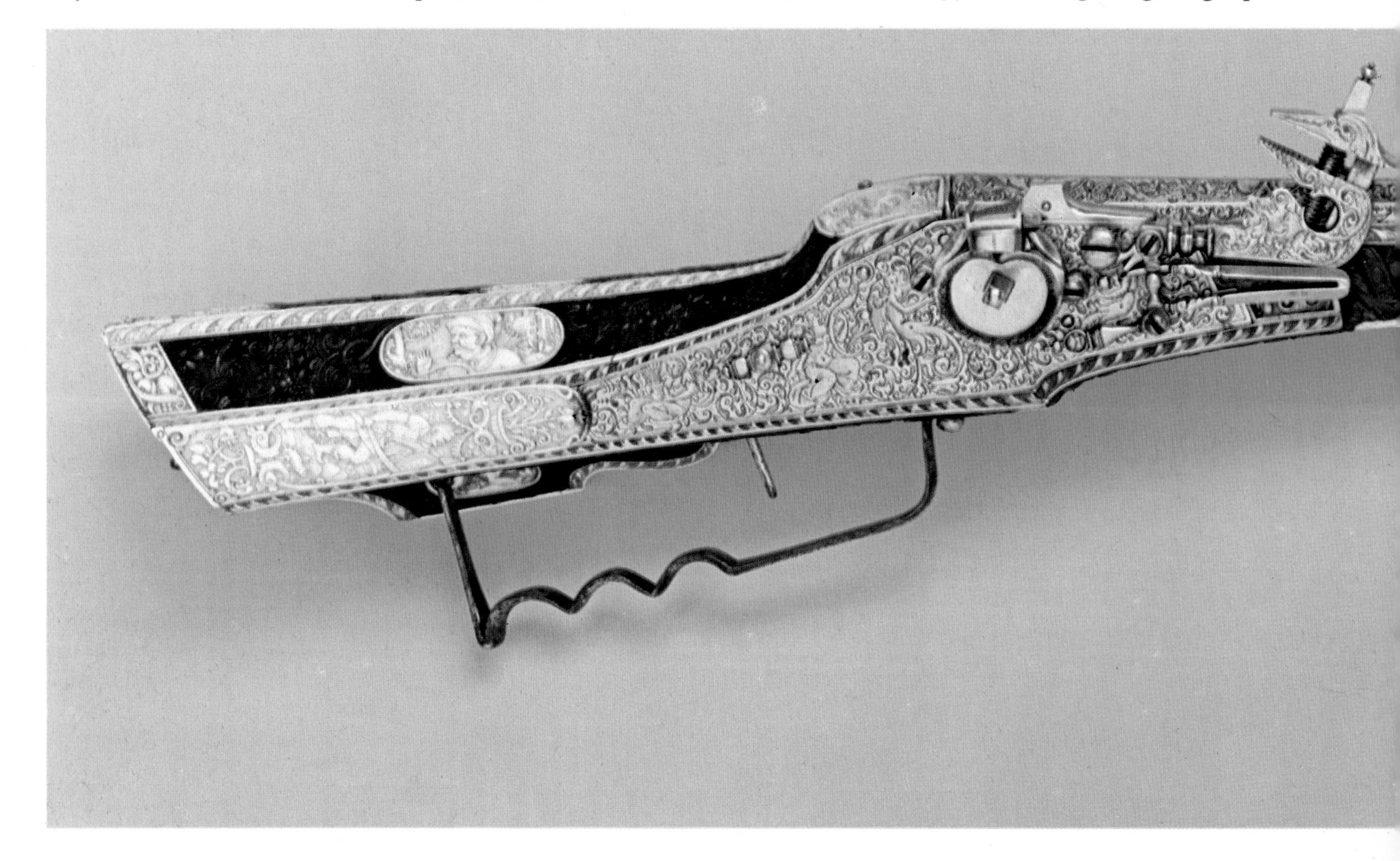

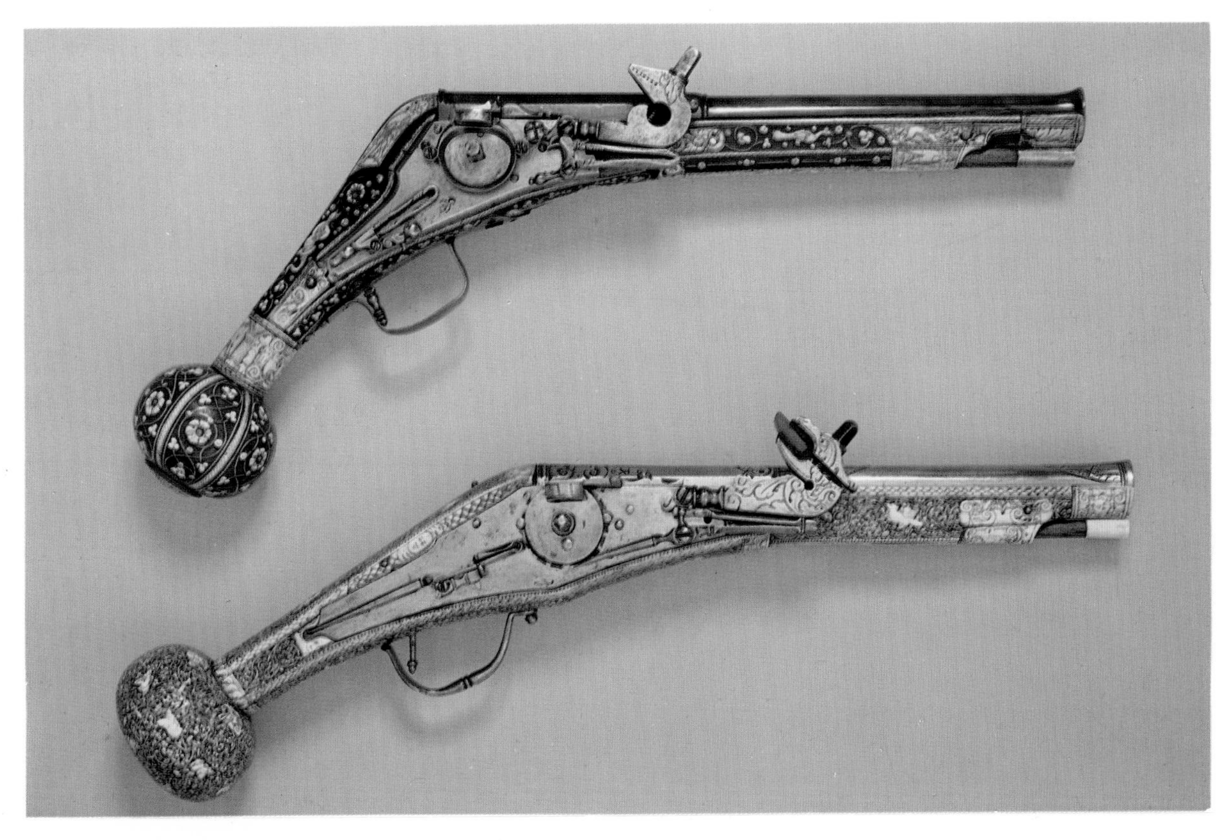

Left **Two ball-butted pistols of characteristic German pattern, the stocks of both inlaid with engraved staghorn. The first example has a lock of French type with a separate mainspring; South German (Nuremberg), dated 1593. The second bears the initials of the stockmaker, B. H., and the barrel is engraved with maker's marks and dated 1579.**

Below **A wheel-lock rifle, the walnut stock applied with carved ebony and staghorn panels, probably by Peter Opel of Regensburg; South German, about 1600.**

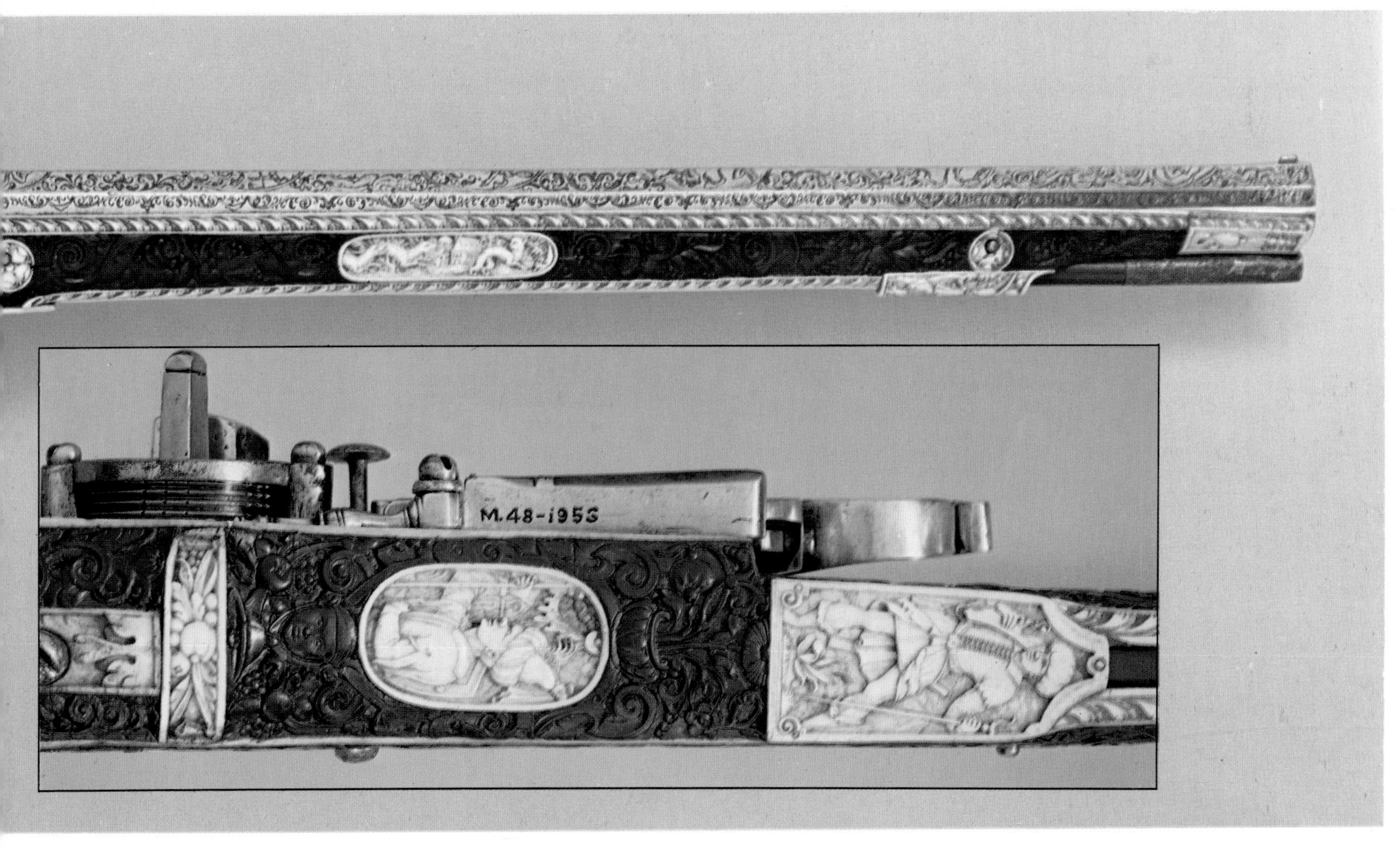

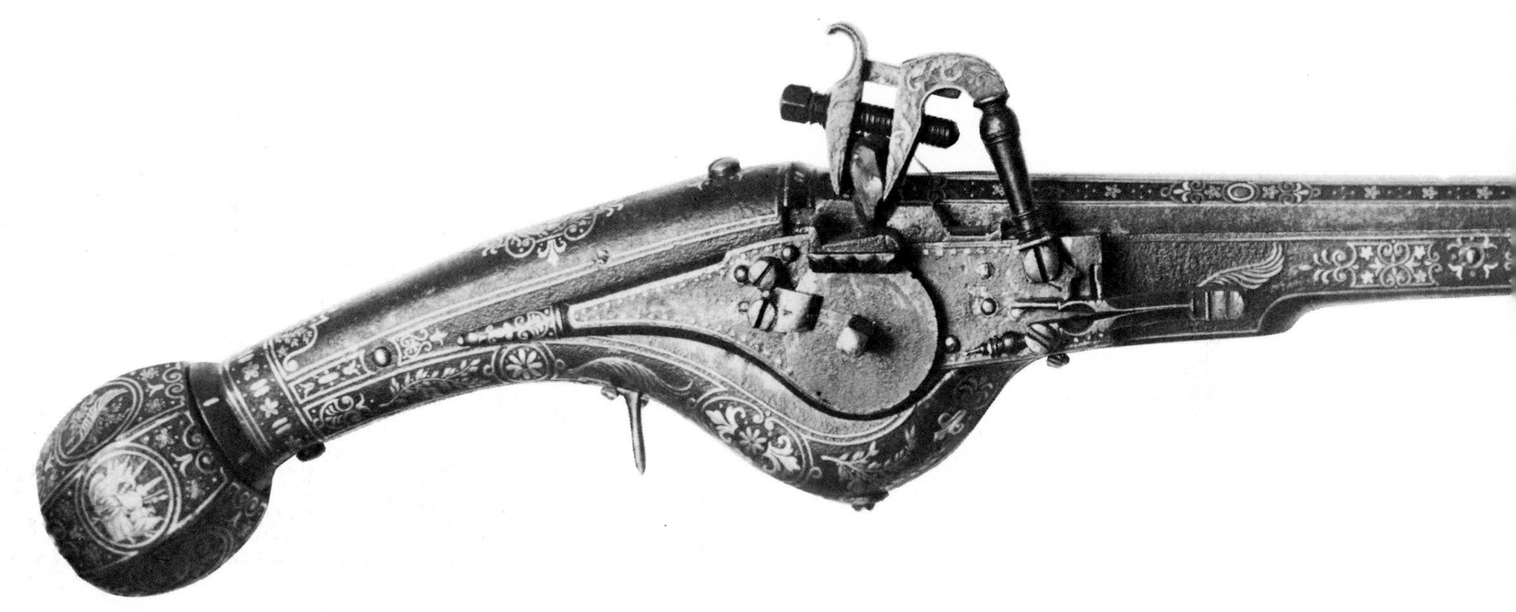

Needless to say, this basic design soon saw improvement. Pan covers which slid open as the cock was put into place were an early step; then came linking of cock and trigger so that as the trigger was pulled, the cock flew forward into contact, the pan cover opened and the wheel revolved. In order to relieve the firer of the need to wind up the wheel after each shot, the 'self-spanning' lock was invented, in which the cock was geared to the wheel in such a manner that pulling it back for a fresh shot would wind up the wheel again; this was an elegant mechanical idea but, due to the powerful leverage needed, was not very practical, and such locks were uncommon.

The wheel-lock was, as might be imagined, rather more expensive than the ordinary matchlock, and for this reason it was not widely adopted as a military arm. Instead, it became the preferred system for sporting and privately owned weapons, and the lock makers and gunsmiths were able to lavish their artistic talent upon wheel-locks. As a result some of the finest specimens of decorated weapons are from the wheel-lock period. Another, less laudable, consequence of the wheel-lock was that weapons could now be carried concealed. It had hardly been practical to try and conceal a matchlock complete with burning match beneath one's clothes, but a cocked and primed wheel-lock was a different matter. So much so that as

LEONARDO'S WHEEL-LOCK

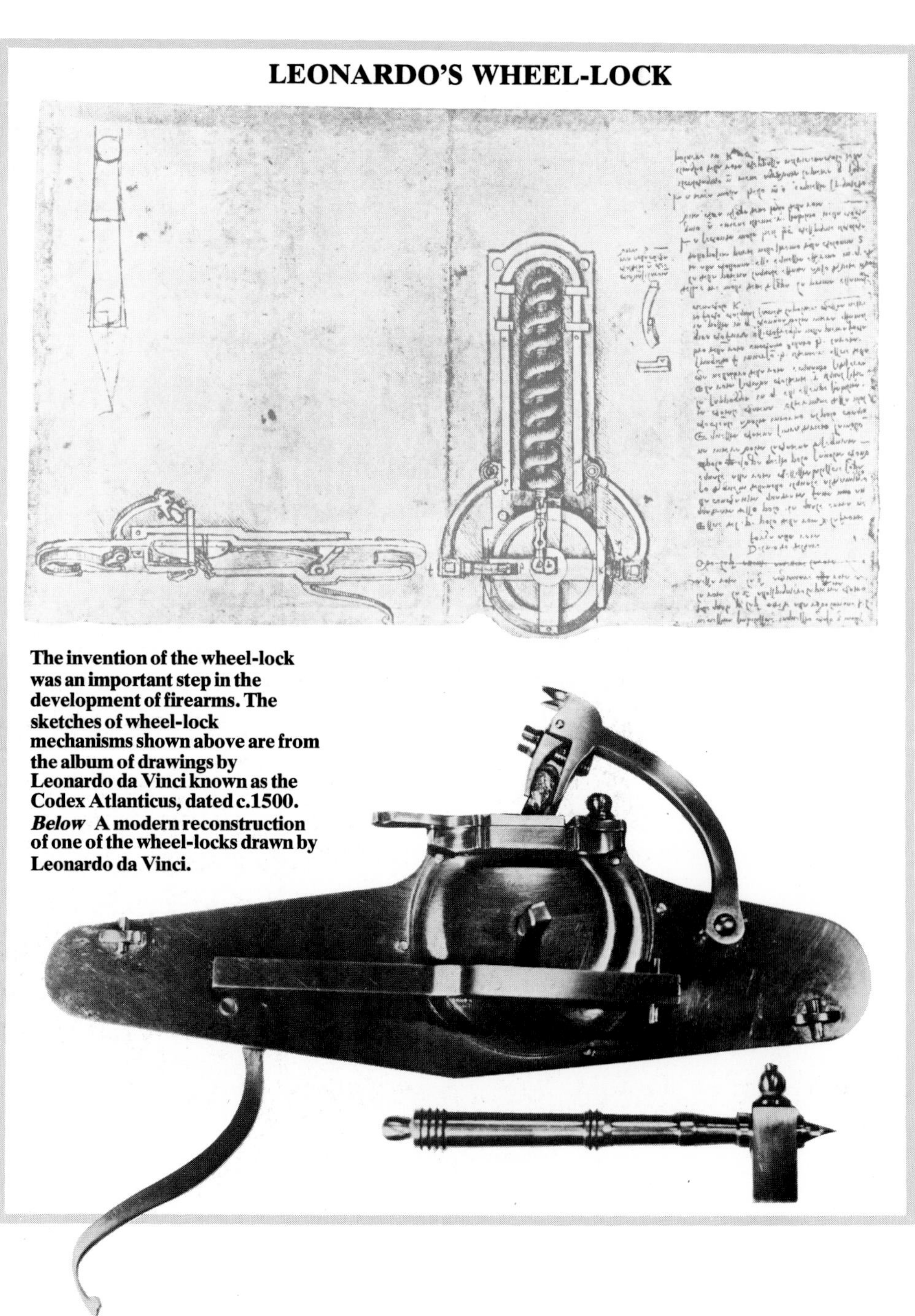

The invention of the wheel-lock was an important step in the development of firearms. The sketches of wheel-lock mechanisms shown above are from the album of drawings by Leonardo da Vinci known as the Codex Atlanticus, dated c.1500. *Below* A modern reconstruction of one of the wheel-locks drawn by Leonardo da Vinci.

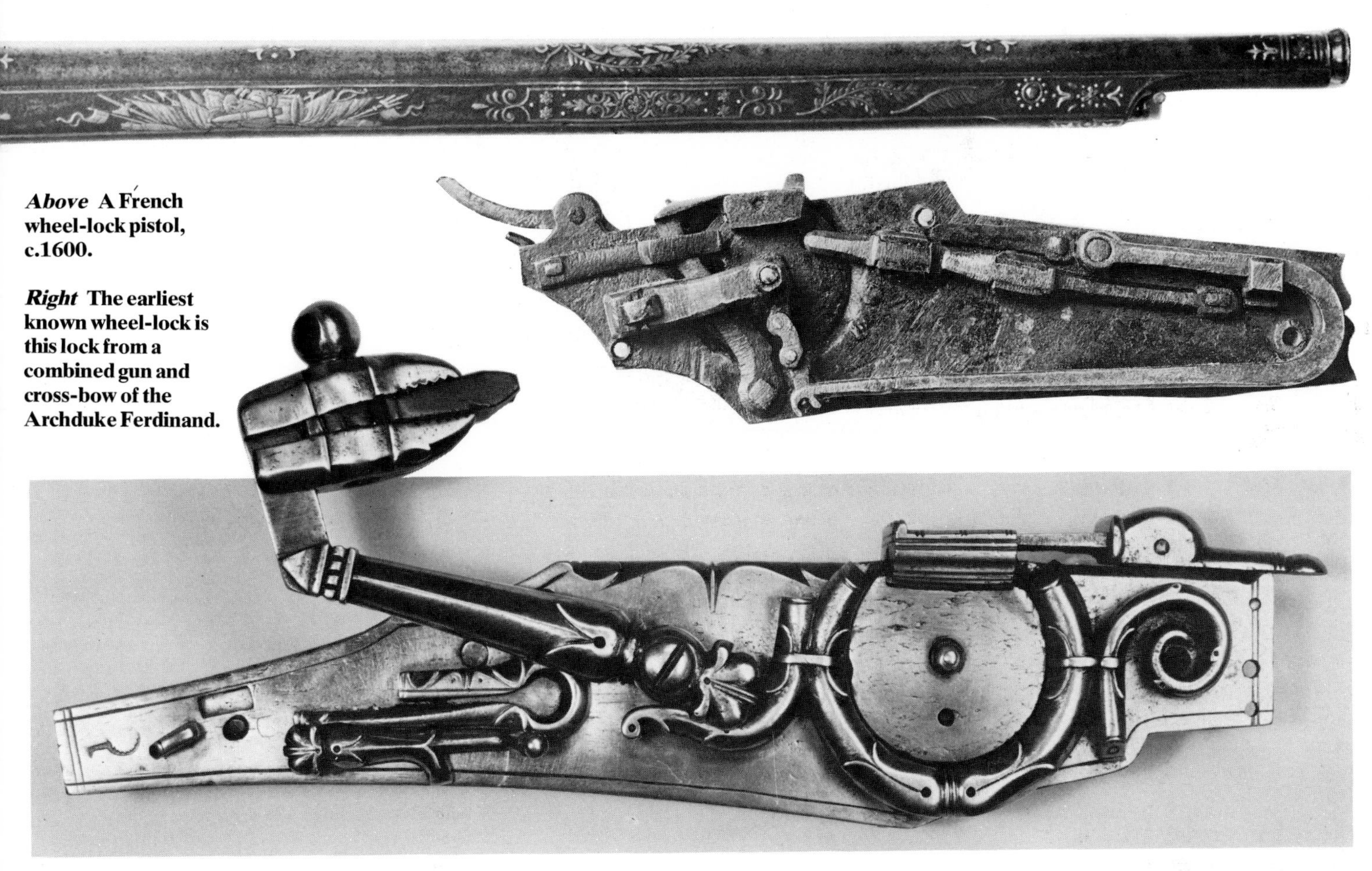

Above **A French wheel-lock pistol, c.1600.**

Right **The earliest known wheel-lock is this lock from a combined gun and cross-bow of the Archduke Ferdinand.**

Above **A self-spanning wheel-lock, c.1540.**

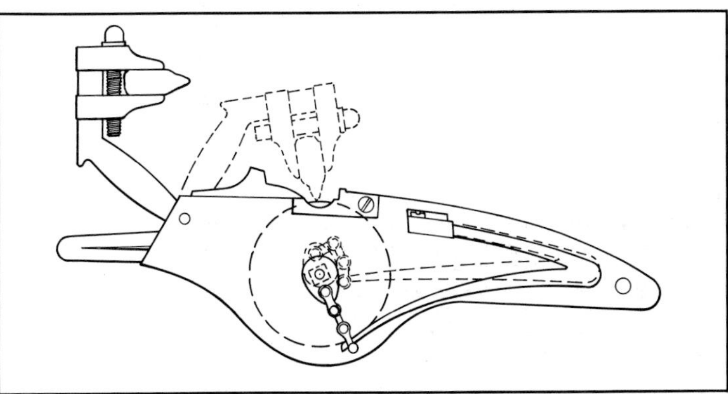

Right **The mechanism of a wheel-lock.**

Below **An interesting French 'pyrites lock' in which a curved arc replaces the serrated wheel.**

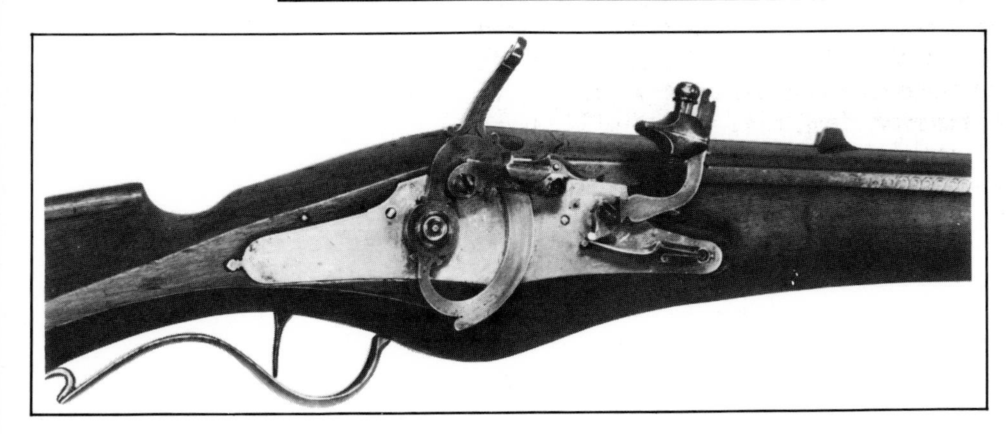

early as 1518 the Emperor Maximilian was being urged to pass laws to forbid the carrying of concealed weapons and 'guns which ignited themselves'.

Since it was inconvenient to attempt to conceal three or four feet of musket or arquebus beneath the coat, these laws suggest that by 1518 the pistol had appeared on the scene, a one-hand short gun capable of ready concealment. However, no dated pistol earlier than about 1560 is known, and it was not until the latter part of the 16th century that the pistol began to make an appearance as a cavalry weapon. Since the cavalry existed in smaller numbers than foot soldiers, and were less likely to damage their expensive weapons, the wheel-lock cavalry pistol soon gained acceptance and led to changes in cavalry tactics to allow the horsemen to discharge their pistols before getting down to business with their swords.

Decorated Stocks and Barrels

The 16th and 17th centuries saw the personal firearm develop from a crude piece of weaponry into a possession reflecting the wealth and prestige of its owner; barrels were often chiselled in relief and gilt, while stocks were fitted with mounts of gilt and inlaid bronze.

Right **A wheel-lock rifle with ivory panels, c.1670.**
Below **Two Turkish flintlocks: 18th century (top) and 17th century (below).**
Below right **Detail of a German wheel-lock pistol, dated 1579.**
Opposite top **An Italian flintlock pistol, c.1690.**
Opposite centre **Designs for pistol ornamentation by Simonin of Paris, 1685.**
Opposite right and bottom **A flintlock pistol by an unknown French gunsmith, c.1690.**

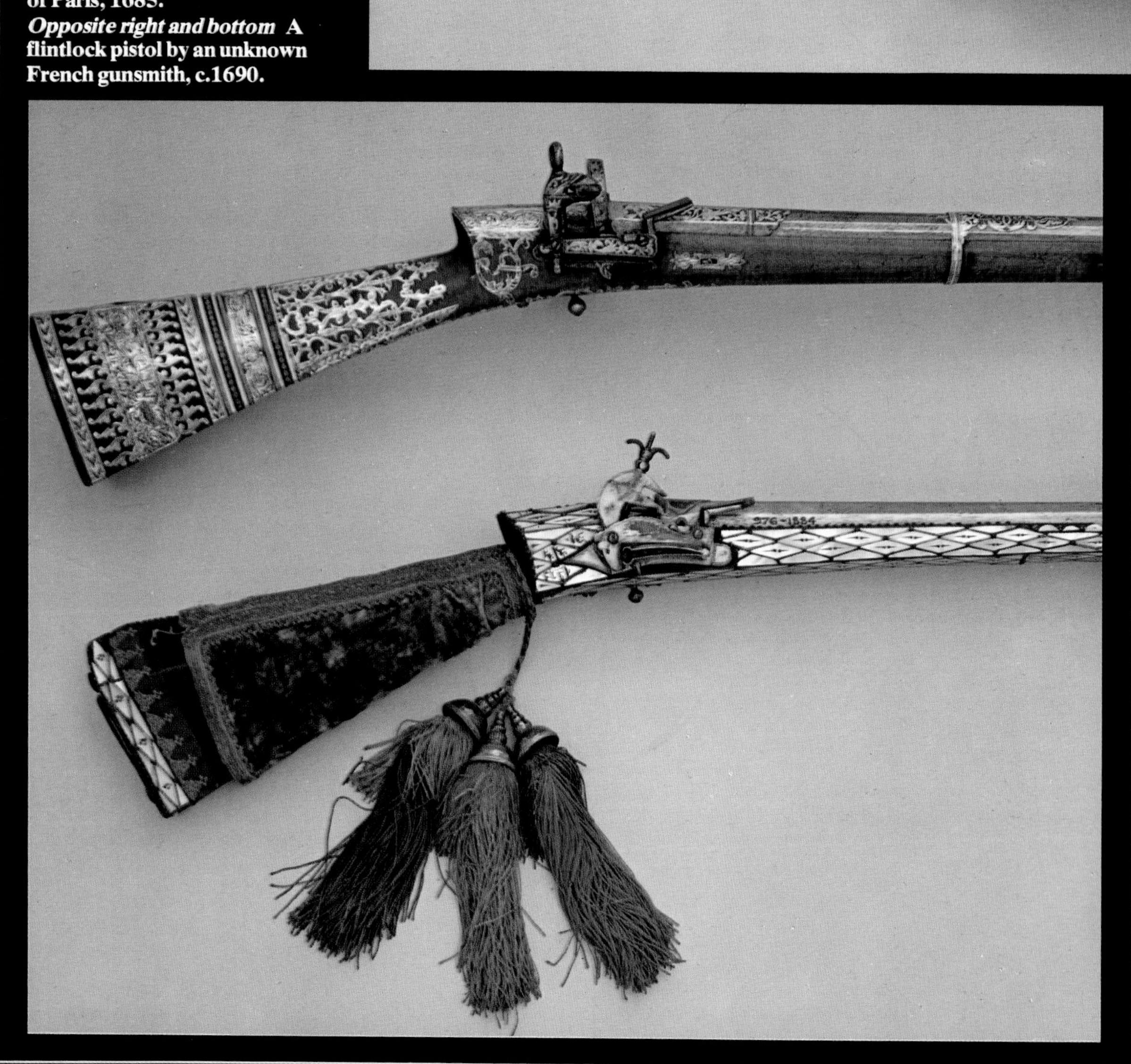

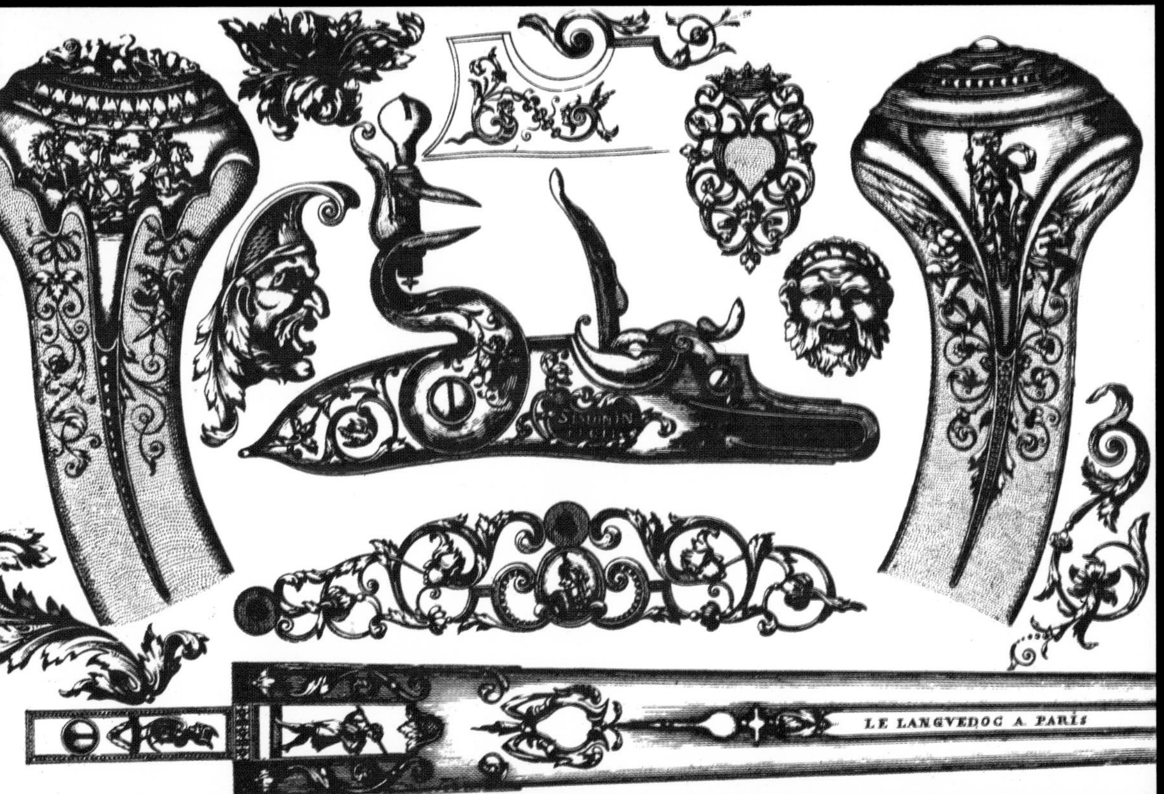
LE LANGVEDOC A. PARIS

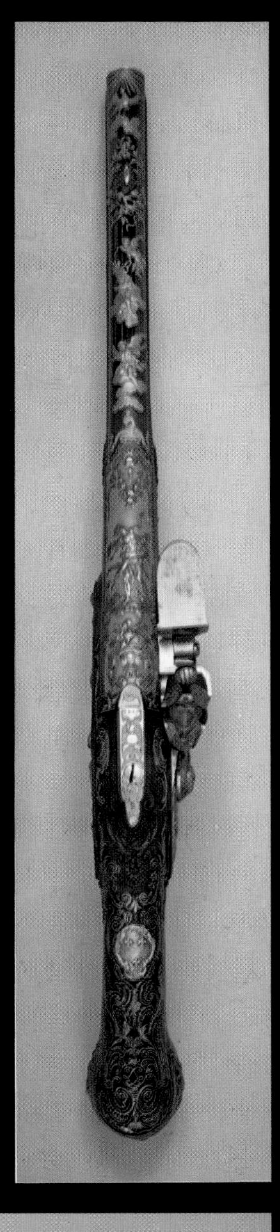

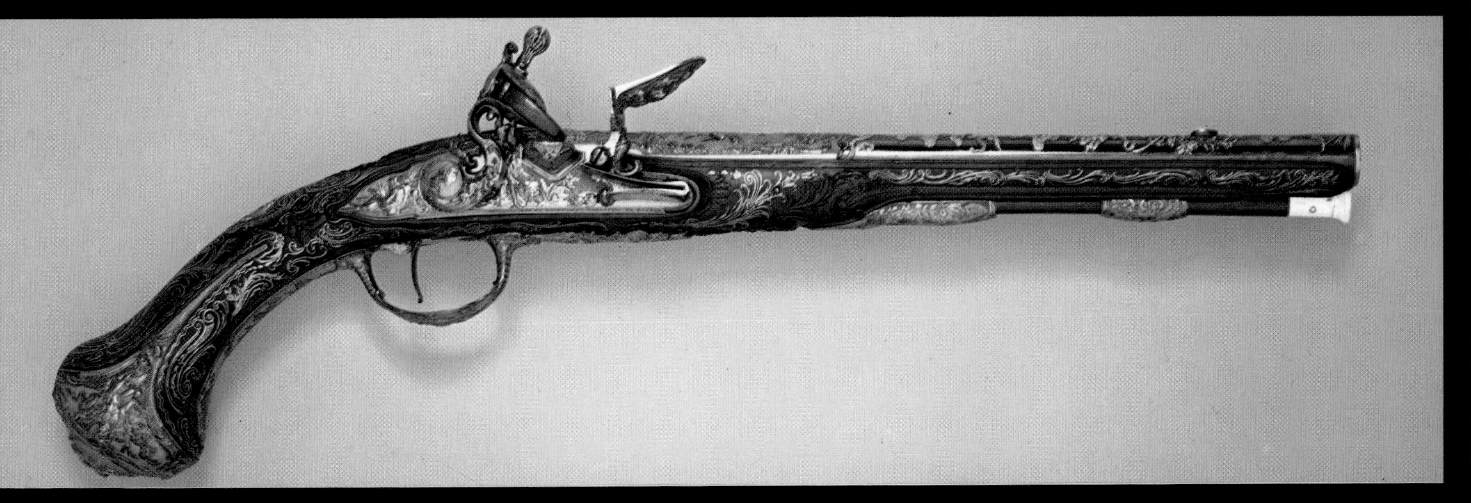

THE SNAPHAUNCE

LATE 16th CENTURY

IN THE 16th CENTURY, as ever since, the sure road to fame and fortune for any weapon designer or manufacturer was to obtain a contract for military supply, and therefore if the wheel-lock was not acceptable to the military, then something cheaper and simpler had to be found.

Once again, a precise time and place cannot be advanced for the snaphaunce, though every indication points to Germany as its birthplace. The basic mechanism was that of a spring-loaded arm, the 'cock', which carried a shaped piece of flint in jaws at its outer end. The pan was now covered by a steel 'frizzen', an arm which was hinged ahead of the pan and which had an upturned and concave face at its free end. The relative positions of cock and frizzen were so arranged that when the cock fell forward, under the impetus of its spring, the flint was driven hard across the curved face of the frizzen so as to strike sparks. At the same time, the curved face of the frizzen and its pivot point led to a complex interplay of forces in which the impact of the cock caused the frizzen arm to fly up so as to allow the struck sparks to pass into the pan and ignite the priming.

These locks were known as 'snaphaunce' locks; the origin of the term is in some doubt. Some writers claim that it comes from the Dutch 'snap Haens', meaning 'hen thief', ascribing this derivation to the early use of the lock by poachers. More likely is the derivation from German: 'Schnapphahn' or 'snapping hammer', which seems more feasible if the German origin of the lock is accepted.

Irrespective of its origin, the snaphaunce soon spread across Europe and certain local preferences and peculiarities emerged. The 'Swedish' or 'Baltic' version, for example, was characterised by an extremely long arm and jaw to the cock, which appears to have been derived from matchlock design. The Spanish lock, sometimes called the 'miquelet' lock, had the frizzen shaped to form a pan cover, so that the powder was not exposed until the actual moment of ignition. The Spanish lock also had a 'half-cock' position as a safety measure. With all snaphaunces the cock was drawn back with the thumb against spring pressure; the lower end of the cock was then rested on a cross-bolt, or 'sear', actuated by the trigger, so that pulling the trigger withdrew the sear and allowed the cock to fall. In the Spanish lock there was a second sear which moved out beneath the toe of the cock as it was pulled back almost as soon as it began to move, and prevented fire being struck if the cock were accidentally slipped during the 'cocking' movement. Once this 'half-cock sear' was under the cock the weapon could be safely carried; the pan cover could be operated; and the trigger could not be pulled, since the trigger sear was not in play. The advantage here was that with the cock at 'half cock', the pan could be primed and the gun loaded and kept loaded in safety. Without the half-cock feature the pan could not be opened if the cock were left forward, but when the weapon was cocked and then loaded, it could only be carried in a most careful fashion for fear of accidental discharge. The Spanish lock's half-cock sear was withdrawn from its blocking position by cam action when the cock was drawn to 'full-cock' position.

The Dutch snaphaunce lock, which was probably derived from the Spanish, separated the frizzen and pan

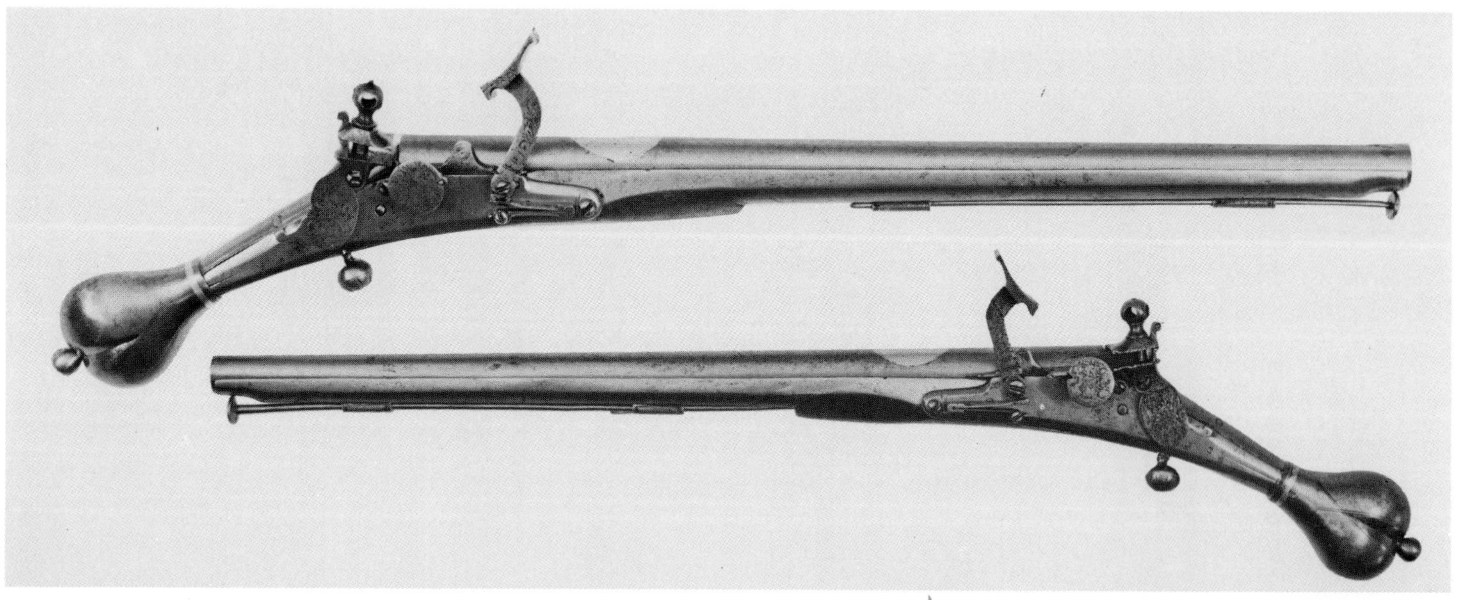

A typical Scottish-made pistol with ball trigger and heart-shaped butt, c.1671.

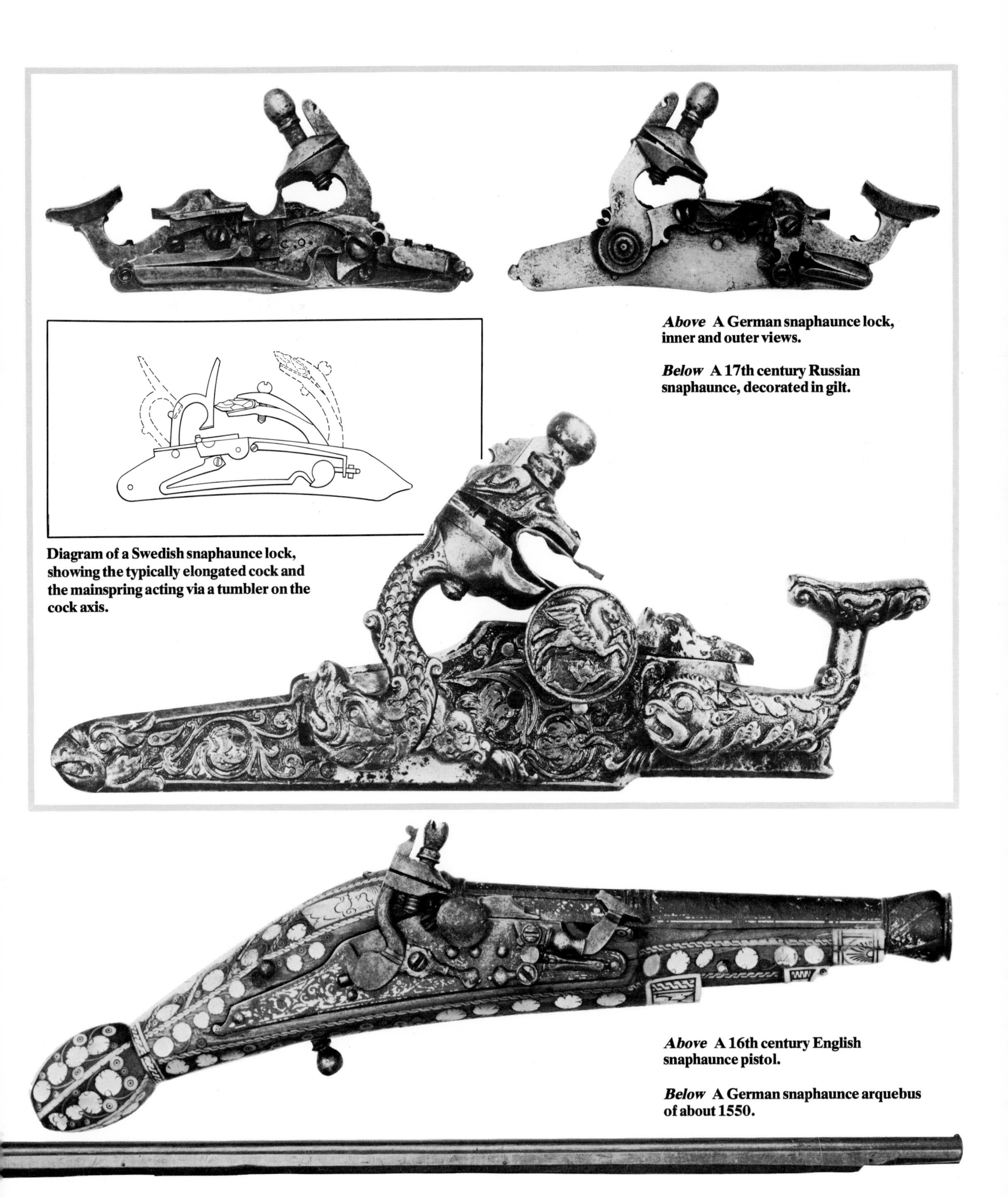

Above **A German snaphaunce lock, inner and outer views.**

Below **A 17th century Russian snaphaunce, decorated in gilt.**

Diagram of a Swedish snaphaunce lock, showing the typically elongated cock and the mainspring acting via a tumbler on the cock axis.

Above **A 16th century English snaphaunce pistol.**

Below **A German snaphaunce arquebus of about 1550.**

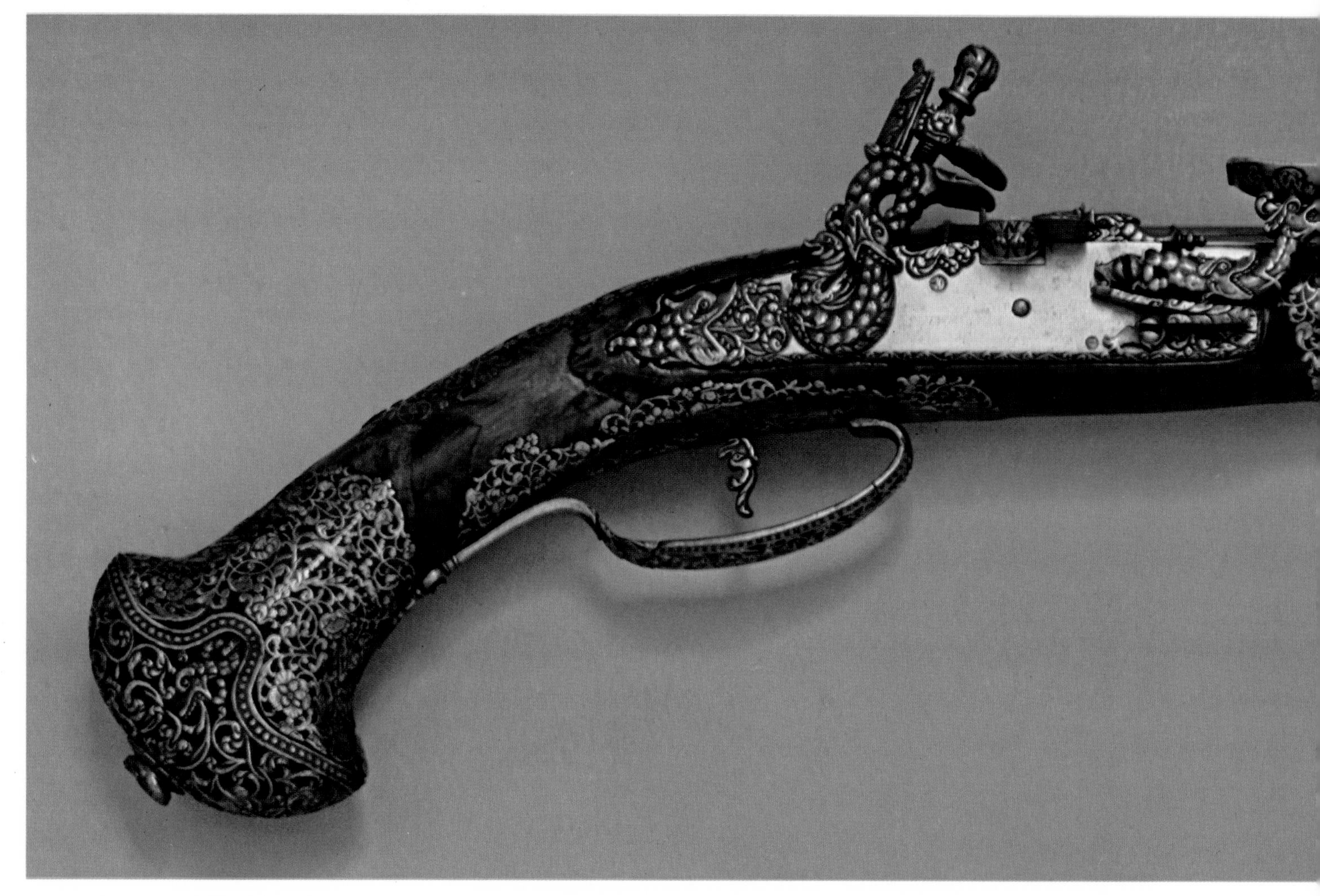

cover into two distinct components and linked the sliding pan cover to the cock by a simple lever. Thus as the cock fell, the pan cover was thrust open in time to receive the sparks. To carry the gun safely, the frizzen could be thrown up, out of the path of the cock, without exposing the priming.

The 'English Lock' used a combined frizzen and pan cover and took its nickname from the sear mechanism in which the cock was a notch in its lower edge into which a 'dog-catch' snapped by spring power as the cock was pulled back. This dog was withdrawn by the action of the trigger.

Some finely decorated snaphaunces are known. Although the snaphaunce lock became the standard method of ignition, it was also incorporated into highly ornamental weapons, carefully made for wealthy patrons.

Above **A snaphaunce holster-pistol, the walnut stock inlaid with mounts of pierced iron, the barrels signed 'Lazarino Cominazzo'; Brescia, about 1650.**
Below **An English snaphaunce musket dated 1588.**
Right **A pair of snaphaunce pistols with mounts of chiselled iron by Giuseppe Guardiani of Anghiari. Italian, late 18th century.**

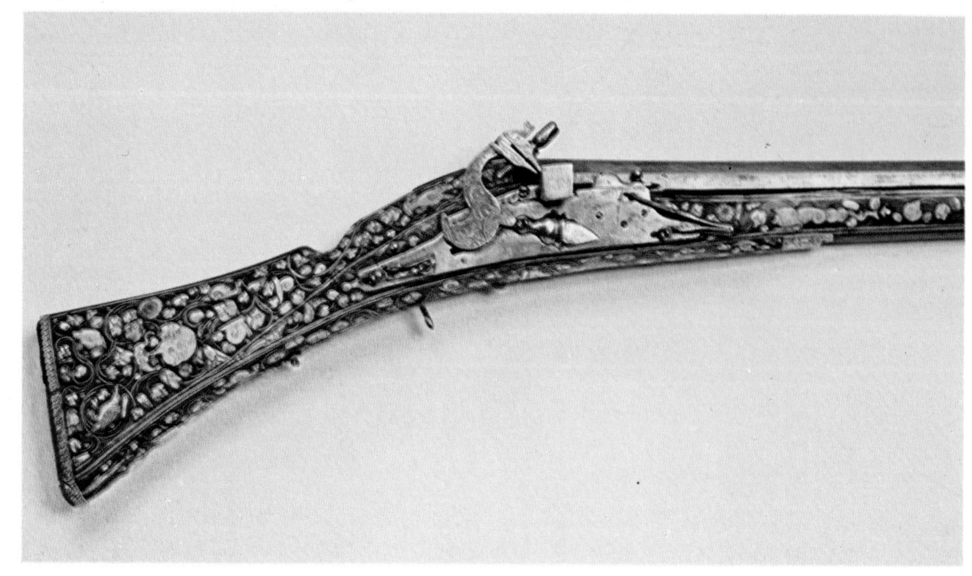

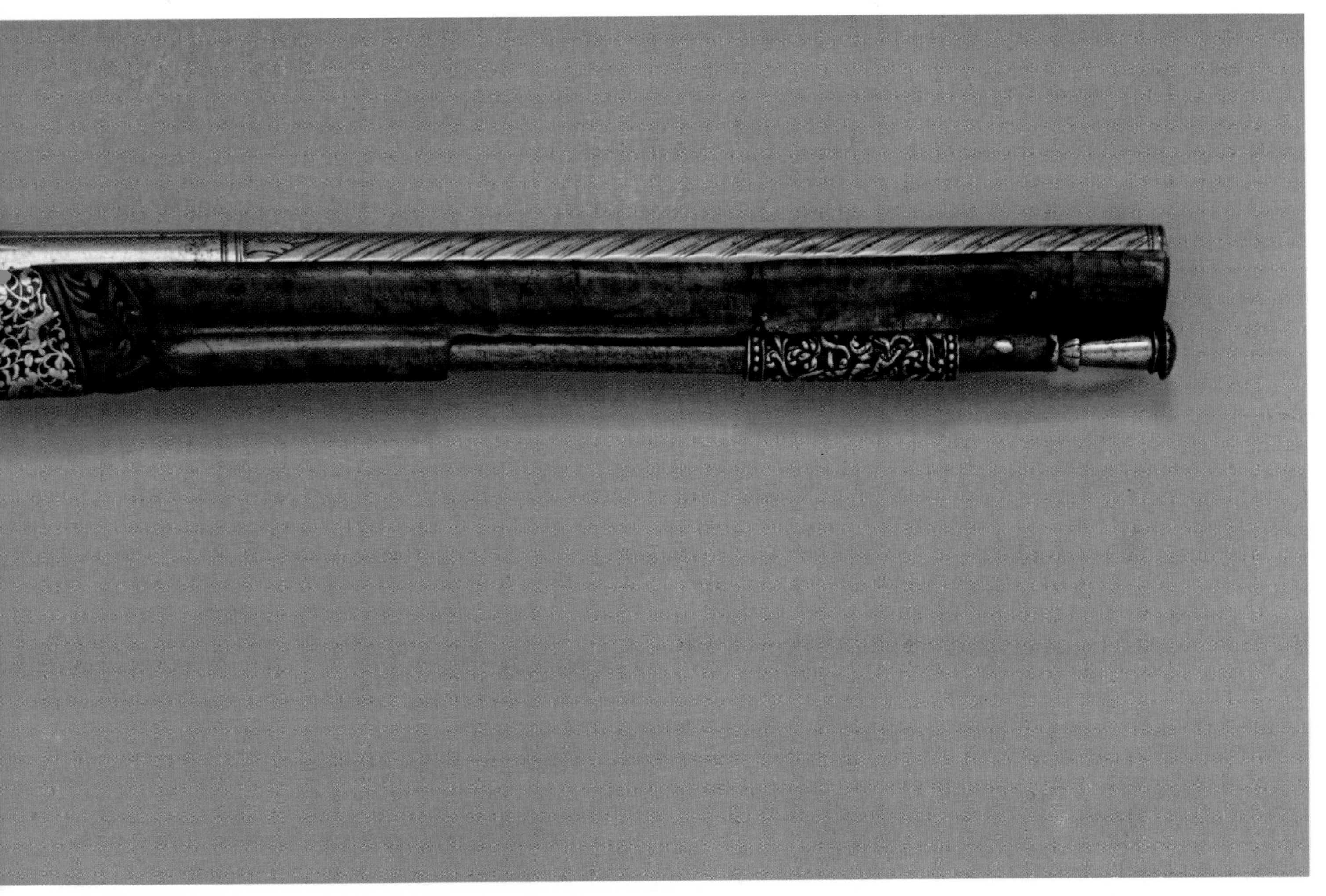

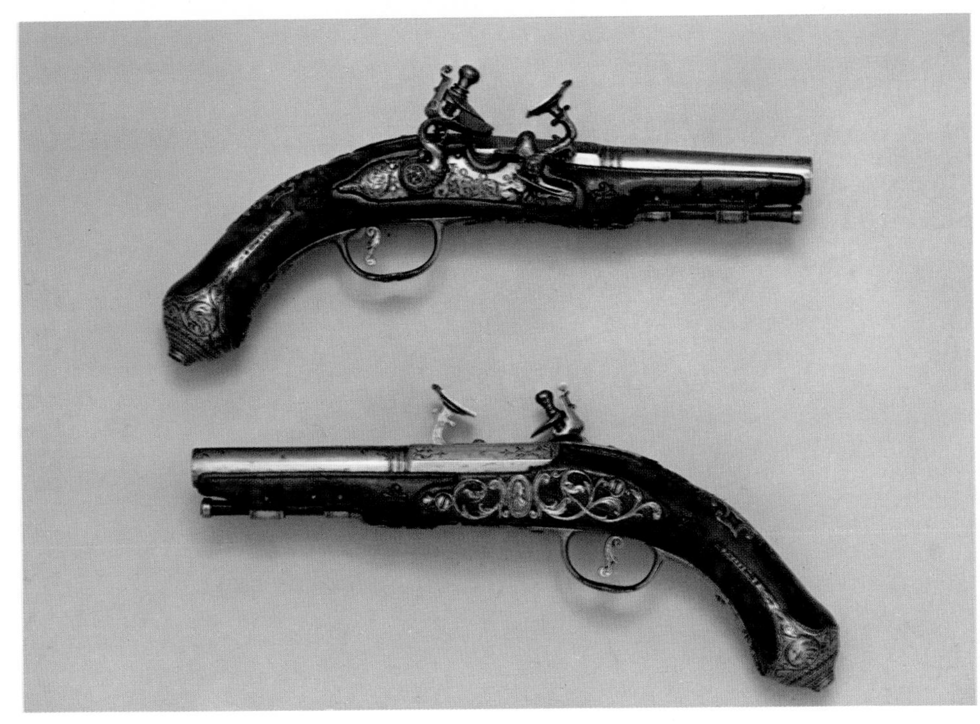

The 20th century concept of conspicuous consumption was present in earlier times in the form of ostentatiousness among the wealthy or the aristocracy. The ownership of beautiful objects has always been desirable in itself, but in earlier times the man who had wealth and power was required to demonstrate it in order to keep it. The lavishly decorated firearm has been common: what better way to flaunt both wealth and power?

Illustrated on these two pages are some of the finer examples of arms using the snaphaunce lock. The musket, inlaid with gold and silver, is English and dates from 1588; the holster pistol, with a stock of walnut inlaid with fretted iron, is from Brescia, Italy, and dates from about 1650; and the two pocket pistols are also Italian, dating from the late 18th century.

THE FLINTLOCK

1620–1635

THE SIMPLICITY and efficiency of the snaphaunce lock rapidly brought it into prominence throughout Europe and it fell to the French to bring together the best features of the various local designs and perfect the 'flintlock' early in the 17th century. The earliest references for perfected flintlocks occur in the 1620–1635 period.

Basically the 'true' flintlock, as perfected, exhibits the following points: the frizzen and pan cover are in one piece, retained in position by a strong spring; the sear moves vertically and engages in a 'tumbler' with two notches to give full and half cock; and the mechanism is entirely concealed on the inner side of the lockplate. The 'tumbler' was a steel cam attached to the axis shaft of the cock, so that movement of the cock was reproduced inside the lock by the tumbler, and the sear could perform its controlling functions by acting upon the tumbler instead of directly on the cock.

The flintlock rapidly assumed the premier position although some gunsmiths remained faithful to the earlier snaphaunce designs and continued to make them for many years. The principal area in which the flintlock prospered was in military firearms; here was a lock which was relatively simple, strong, not expensive, and as reliable as could be expected, and which put an end to the dangers of carrying burning slowmatch.

With the form of lock more of less settled, improvements and perfections appeared. Flint 'knapping' or forming became a major industry in those parts of the world where particularly sound flint occurred: Brandon in England, Cher in France, the Southern Tyrol and Transylvania were noted for the quality of their flints and exported them by the barrel. A good flint was generally considered to last for about fifty shots, after which it was generally discarded, since attempts to put a new edge on it were seldom successful. The actual fixing of the flint into the cock was quite a delicate matter, as this extract from the English *Exercises of the Firelock* shows: 'In fixing flints, no uniform mode should be attempted; the flat side must be placed either upwards or downwards according to the size and shape of the flint and also according to the proportion which the cock bears in height to the frizzen, which varies in different muskets. This is observed by letting the cock gently down and observing where the flint strikes the frizzen, which ought to be at a distance of about one third from the top. Most diligent observation ought at the same time to be made whether every part of the edge of the flint comes into contact with the frizzen, so as to strike out fire from the whole surface. Each particular flint, therefore, requires its own particular mode of fixing so as to accommodate it to the particular proportions and conformations of each lock. Whenever a piece has been fired, the first opportunity should be taken to examining whether the flint remains good, and fixed as it ought to be, and no time should be lost in correcting whatever may be found amiss. . .'

An important innovation which accompanied the flintlock was the prepared cartridge. Since the earliest days the soldier had been provided with a flask of powder and a pouch of bullets, and he loaded these items individually. An early attempt at standardisation had been the 'cartouche', a small container which held one bullet and sufficient powder for one loading. But now the complete bullet and powder combination was wrapped in a tube of paper. The use of the cartridge can be seen in this extract from the *Exercise of the Firelock:*

'Upon the command "Prime and Load", make a quarter face to the right . . . at the same time bringing the

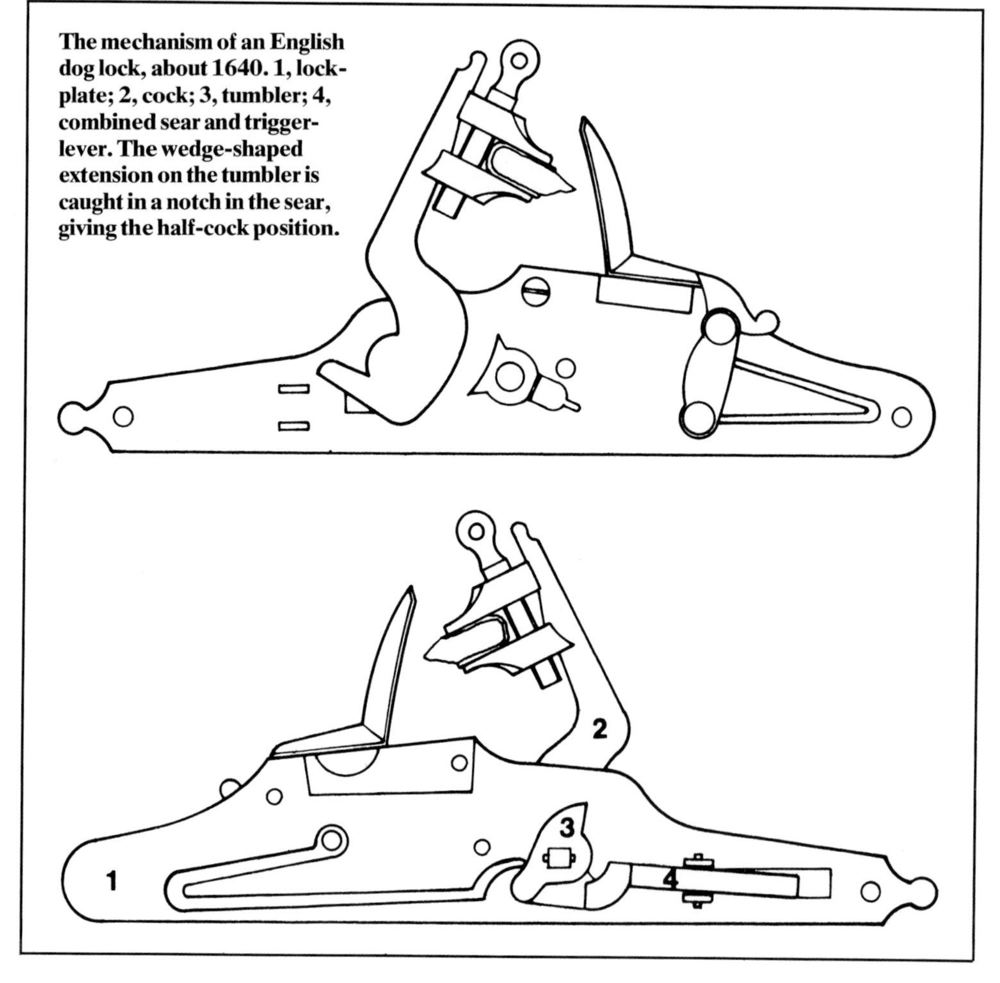

The mechanism of an English dog lock, about 1640. 1, lockplate; 2, cock; 3, tumbler; 4, combined sear and trigger-lever. The wedge-shaped extension on the tumbler is caught in a notch in the sear, giving the half-cock position.

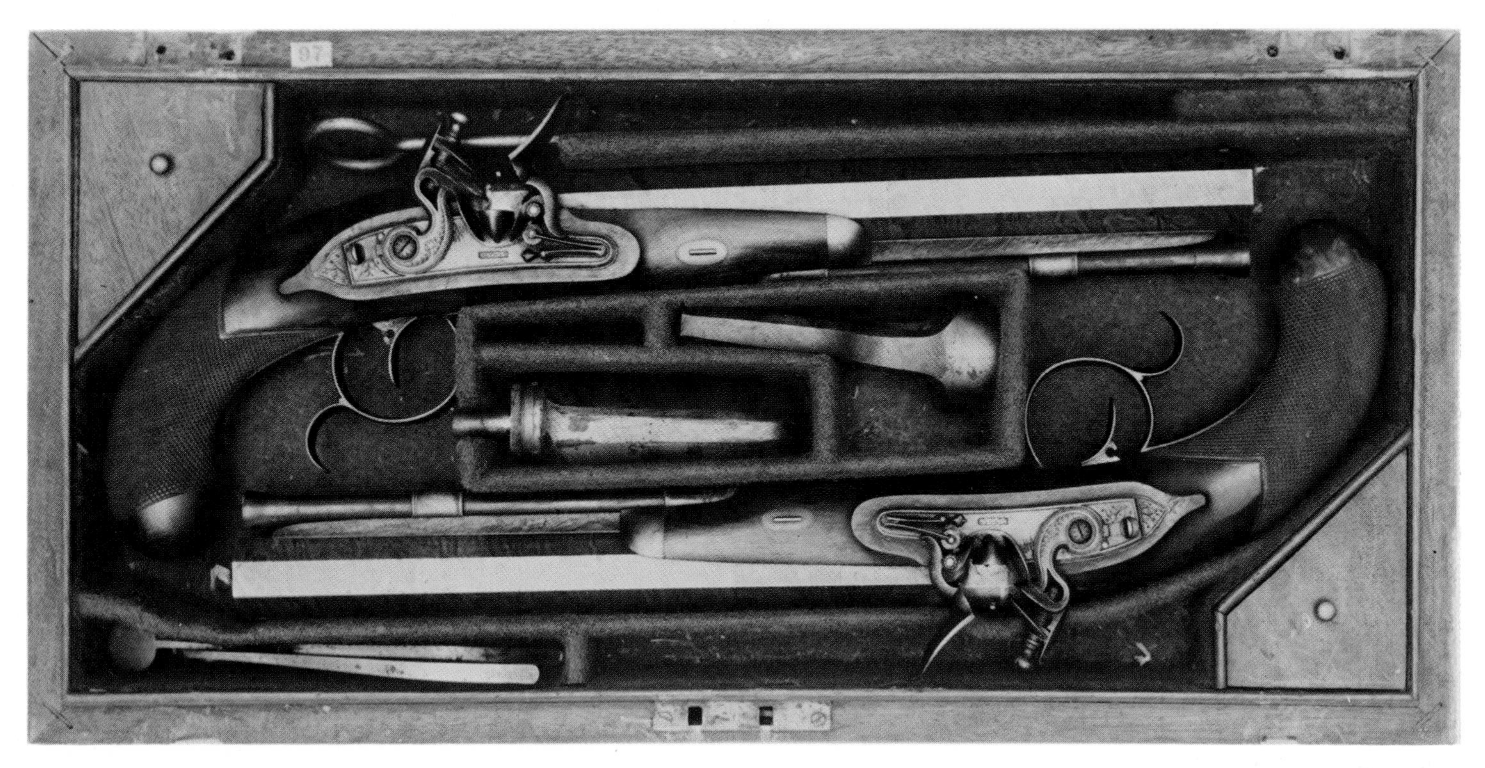

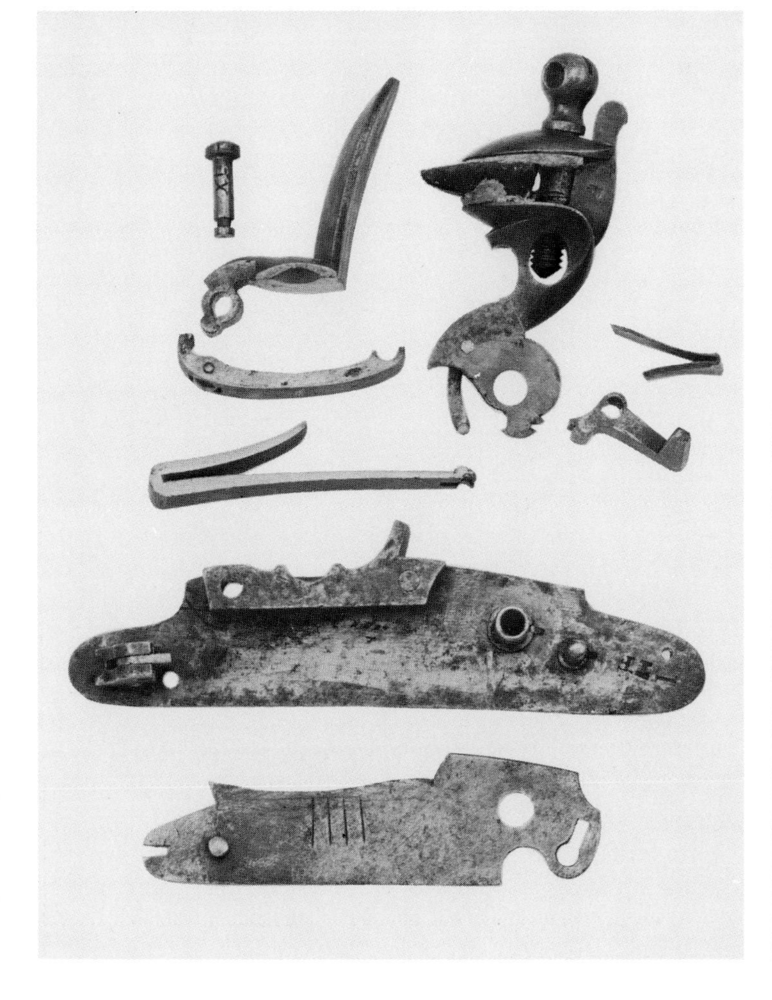

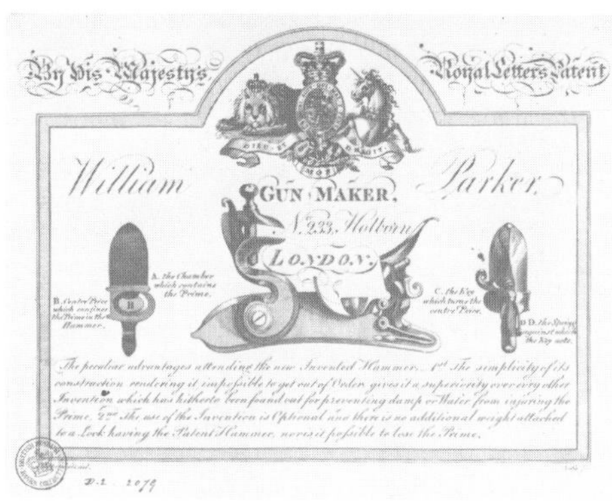

Above **A pair of flintlock duelling pistols, cased, by Nock, c.1800**
Left **A gunmaker's label of 1809.**
Far left **Components of Nock's Screwless Lock from an English cavalry pistol c.1800.**
Below **Detail of the lock from a gun of Louis XIII made by le Bourgeoys c.1620.**

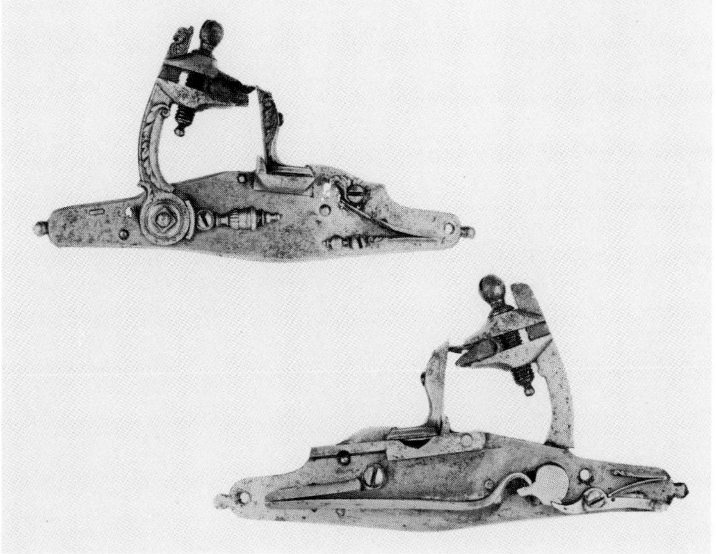

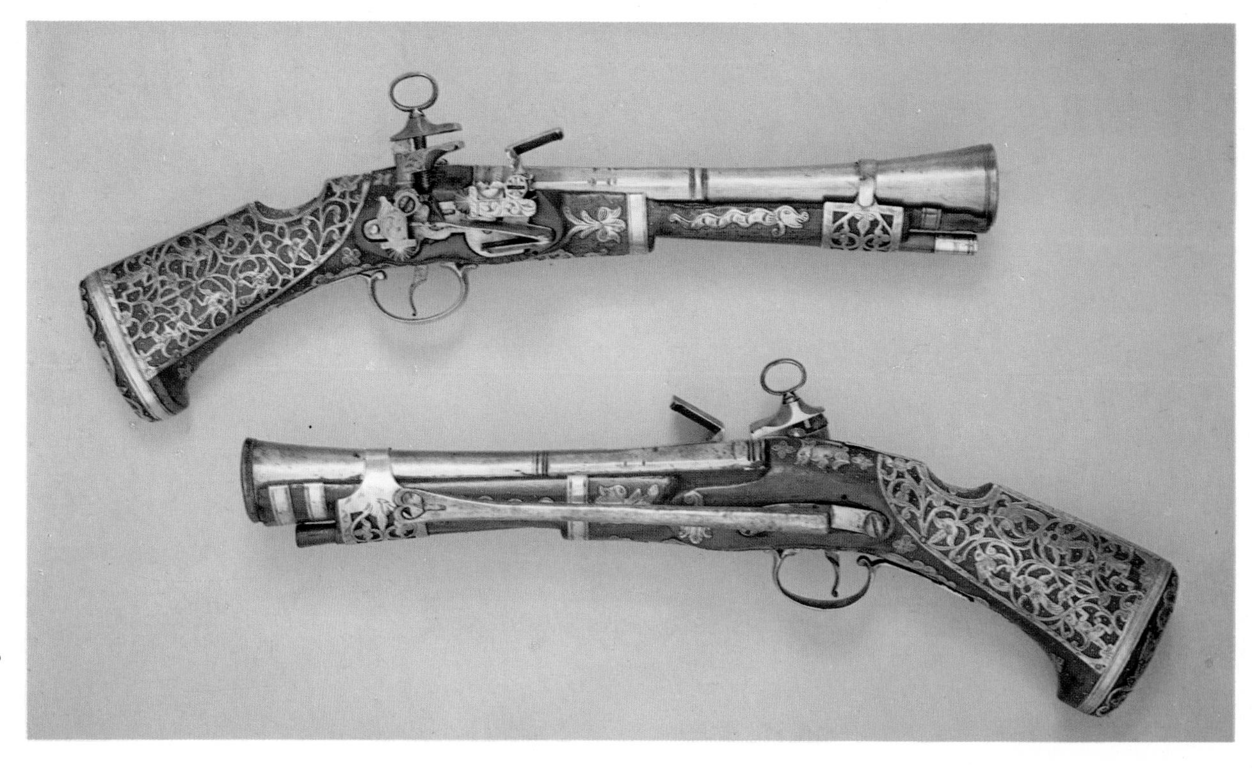

Right **Two Spanish miquelet-lock blunderbusses, c.1690.**

Below right **A French gun of about 1770, with mounts of silver and gilded iron, the barrel inlaid with brass.**

Below **An early German cartridge box of embossed iron, with loops for attaching to the belt, c.1550.**

Right **A German powder flask of staghorn mounted in silver gilt.**

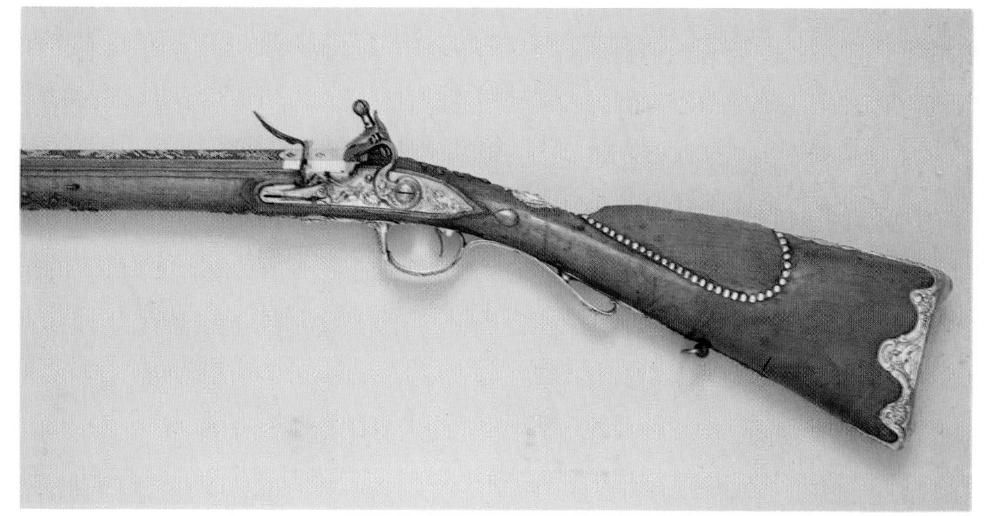

firelock down to the priming position . . . Open the pan. . .'

'Upon the command "Handle Cartridge", 1st draw the cartridge from the pouch, 2nd bring it to the mouth, holding between the forefinger and thumb, and bite off the top of the cartridge.'

'Upon the command "Prime", 1st, shake out some powder into the pan and place the last three fingers on the hammer. 2nd shut the pan. . .'

'Upon the command "About", turn the piece nimbly round to the loading position . . . Place the butt upon the ground without noise, raise the elbow square with the shoulder, and shake the powder into the barrel. . .'

'Upon the command "Draw Ramrods" force the ramrod half out and seize it back-handed exactly in the middle. 2nd, draw it entirely out, turning it at the same time to the front, put one inch into the barrel.'

On the command "Ram Down the Cartridge" . . . push the ramrod well down to the bottom and strike it two very quick strokes with the ramrod.'

NICHOLAS BOUTET

A foremost French gunmaker Nicholas Boutet (below) who specialised in decorated firearms. Examples of his work are (top) a pair of pistols, c.1820, and (below) a garniture of arms presented to Napoleon in 1797.

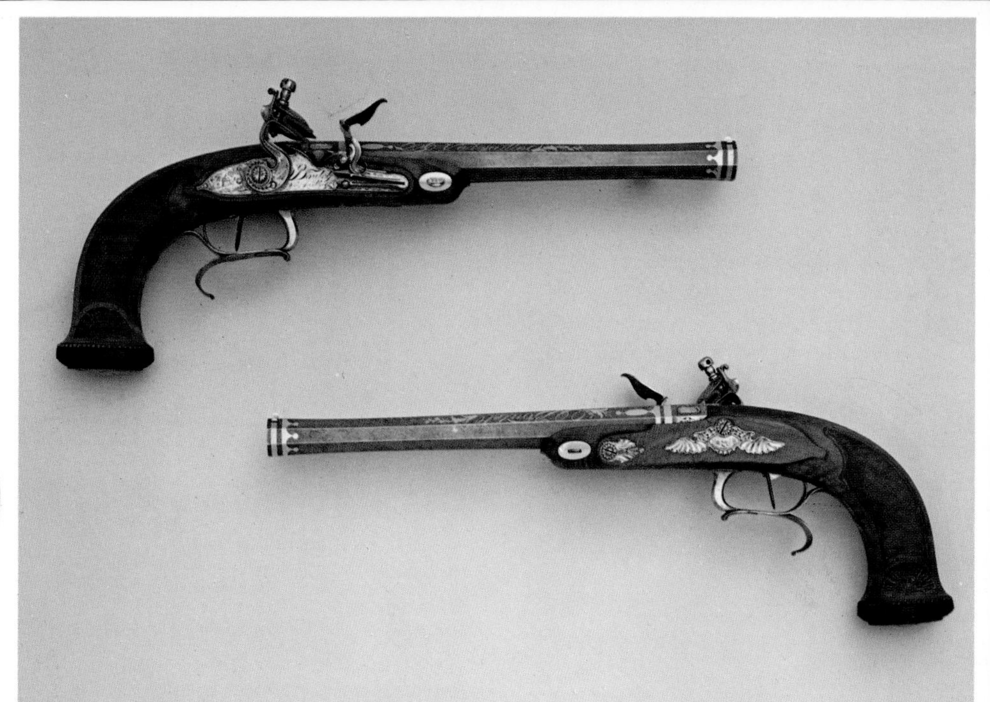

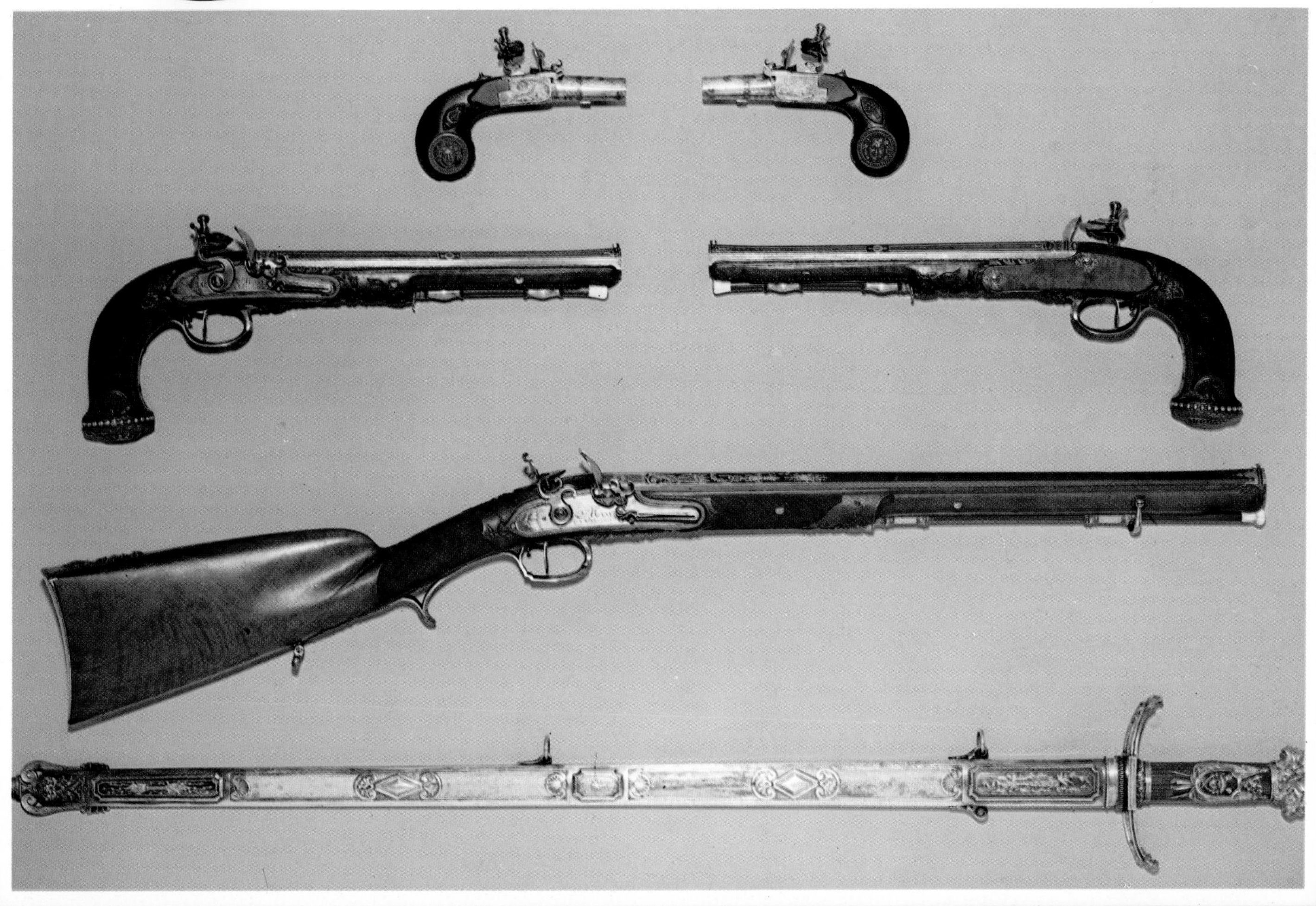

THE PERCUSSION PRINCIPLE

EARLY 19th CENTURY

THE FLINTLOCK, for all its virtues, had one inherent fault; its action was not instantaneous, but could be distinguished as three separate events: first the fall of the cock and striking of sparks; second the ignition of the priming; and third the explosion of the cartridge and ejection of the bullet. In the military application this led to long and intensive training of the recruit, since his normal reaction was to flinch as the priming fired, thus disturbing his aim before the cartridge exploded. In the sporting application the snap of the flint and the flash of the priming often alerted the game, which moved with lightning reaction and was no longer there when the bullet or shot arrived. Hunters became adept at forecasting how far and in which direction the game would spring or fly and aimed-off accordingly, but it turned hunting into a game of chance instead of a reliable method of filling the pot.

Among the hunters who suffered thus was the Reverend Alexander Forsyth of Belhelvie, Aberdeenshire. As well as ministering to his flock, Forsyth devoted his time to chemistry, mechanics and shooting, and he began to apply his mind to the problem of making a weapon capable of instantaneous discharge. In 1800 Edward Howard of the Royal Society had discovered fulminate of mercury, a sensitive substance which, when struck, detonated violently: doubtless Forsyth had heard of this, and he began making his own experiments. In 1807 he patented a system of ignition which relied upon a 'detonating powder' composed largely of potassium chlorate.

In Forsyth's lock, the frizzen and pan were replaced by a small revolving magazine resembling a flask—it became known as the 'scent bottle lock' from its shape—which contained a supply of detonating powder. This magazine pivoted around an axis which was bored through the side of the gun barrel to provide a vent into the chamber. The flint-carrying cock

The Reverend Alexander James Forsyth of Belhelvie, inventor of the percussion firearm.

was now replaced by a simple hammer. The gun was loaded with powder and shot in the usual way, and then the magazine was revolved a half-turn about its axis. This brought the powder receptacle above the vent and a small measure of detonating powder dropped down and charged the vent. The magazine was then turned back half a turn, which took the magazine section down to the 'blind' side of the vent and positioned a loosely-held pin above the powder in the vent. On pulling the trigger the hammer fell, striking the pin; this was driven down into the vent, crushing the powder and exploding it. The resulting flame ran down the vent and fired the gunpowder charge. There were some very surprised birds around Belhelvie in 1807.

Forsyth attempted to interest the government in his lock for military use, and he attracted the attention of the Master General of the Ordnance. For two years he had the use of a workshop in the Tower of London, but on a change of Master Generals his contract was terminated. He then set up a company, with James Purdey, a prominent gunsmith, and put the percussion lock on the market with considerable commercial success.

It is questionable whether any other single innovation in the history of firearms is as significant as Forsyth's percussion principle, for without it much of the subsequent developments—metallic cartridges, automatic weapons, breech loading—could never have taken place. It marks the watershed between the long and slow development of the muzzle-loading arm—1326 to 1807—and the rapid and manifold developments of breech-loading and rapid-firing arms of all descriptions, much of which development was fundamentally completed by 1900.

Once Forsyth had shown the way, practical gunsmiths were quick to make improvements. Forsyth and Purdey changed the 'scent bottle' lock to a similar sliding pattern, linked to the hammer; as the hammer was cocked, so the magazine slid forward, bringing a firing pin into position to be struck by the hammer. Similar locks were produced by gunsmiths on the continent, but the use of loose detonating powder had its drawbacks and alternative systems of priming were soon to appear.

One early idea was to make up small pills of powder, coating them with varnish or gum. These were placed in the vent and struck by the hammer. Such a system came, of course, from contemporary apothecary's practice, as did an alternative system of sealing pinches of powder between two discs of paper, which has survived to this day in the caps or 'amorces' used by children in toy guns.

Stemming from the paper disc system came the 'tape' system invented by Maynard, an American dentist, in which small patches of powder were stuck to a paper or linen tape which could be pulled from a magazine and laid across the vent as required.

Another ingenious system was the placing of the powder at the closed end of a small copper tube. The open end was thrust into the vent, and the hammer fell so as to crush the closed

Above **A Forsyth sporting gun in its case.**

Right **The label from the sporting gun case, showing details of the 'scent bottle' lock and instructions for its use.**

Overleaf **A pair of percussion pistols in a mahogany case with plated turn-off barrels and walnut stocks inlaid with silver. Signed 'Egg London', about 1830.**

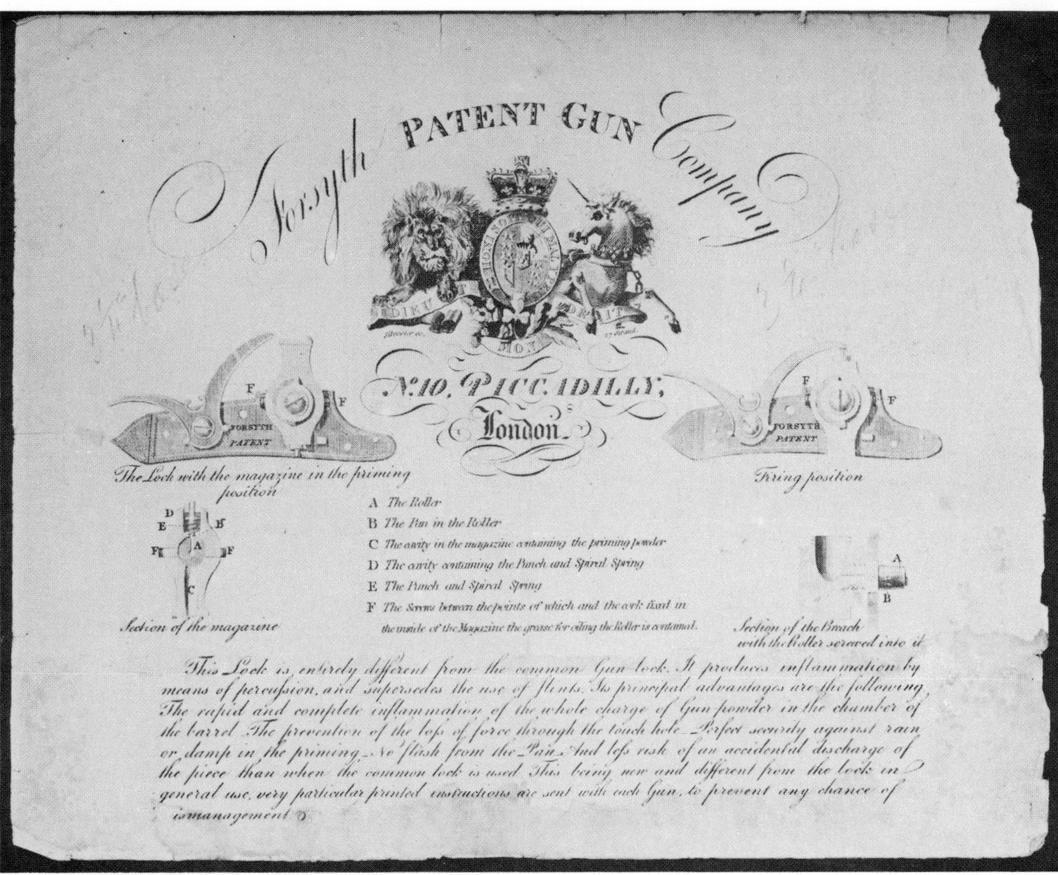

Forsyth PATENT GUN Company

No. 10, PICCADILLY;
London.

The Lock with the magazine in the priming position

Firing position

A *The Roller*
B *The Pin in the Roller*
C *The cavity in the magazine containing the priming powder*
D *The cavity containing the Punch and Spiral Spring*
E *The Punch and Spiral Spring*
F *The Screws between the points of which and the cork fixed in the inside of the Magazine the grease for oiling the Roller is contained.*

Section of the magazine

Section of the Breach with the Roller screwed into it

This Lock is entirely different from the common Gun lock. It produces inflammation by means of percussion, and supersedes the use of flints. Its principal advantages are the following, The rapid and complete inflammation of the whole charge of Gun powder in the chamber of the barrel. The prevention of the loss of force through the touch hole. Perfect security against rain or damp in the priming. No flash from the Pan. And less risk of an accidental discharge of the piece than when the common lock is used. This being new and different from the lock in general use, very particular printed instructions are sent with each Gun, to prevent any chance of mismanagement.

THE FORSYTH LOCK
1 is the magazine, which revolves around 2, the vent. The hammer 3 strikes the firing pin 4 to ignite the powder deposited in the vent.

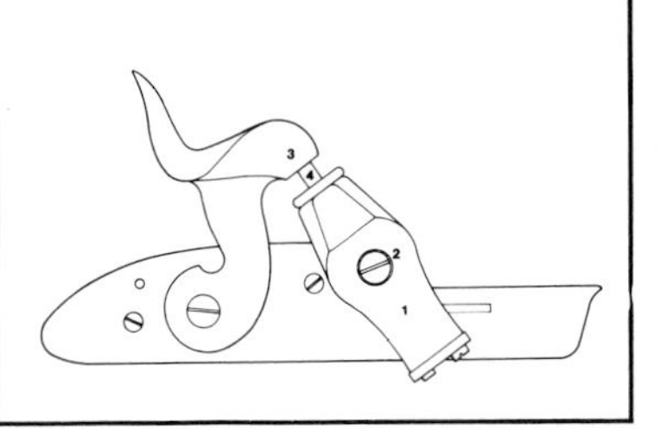

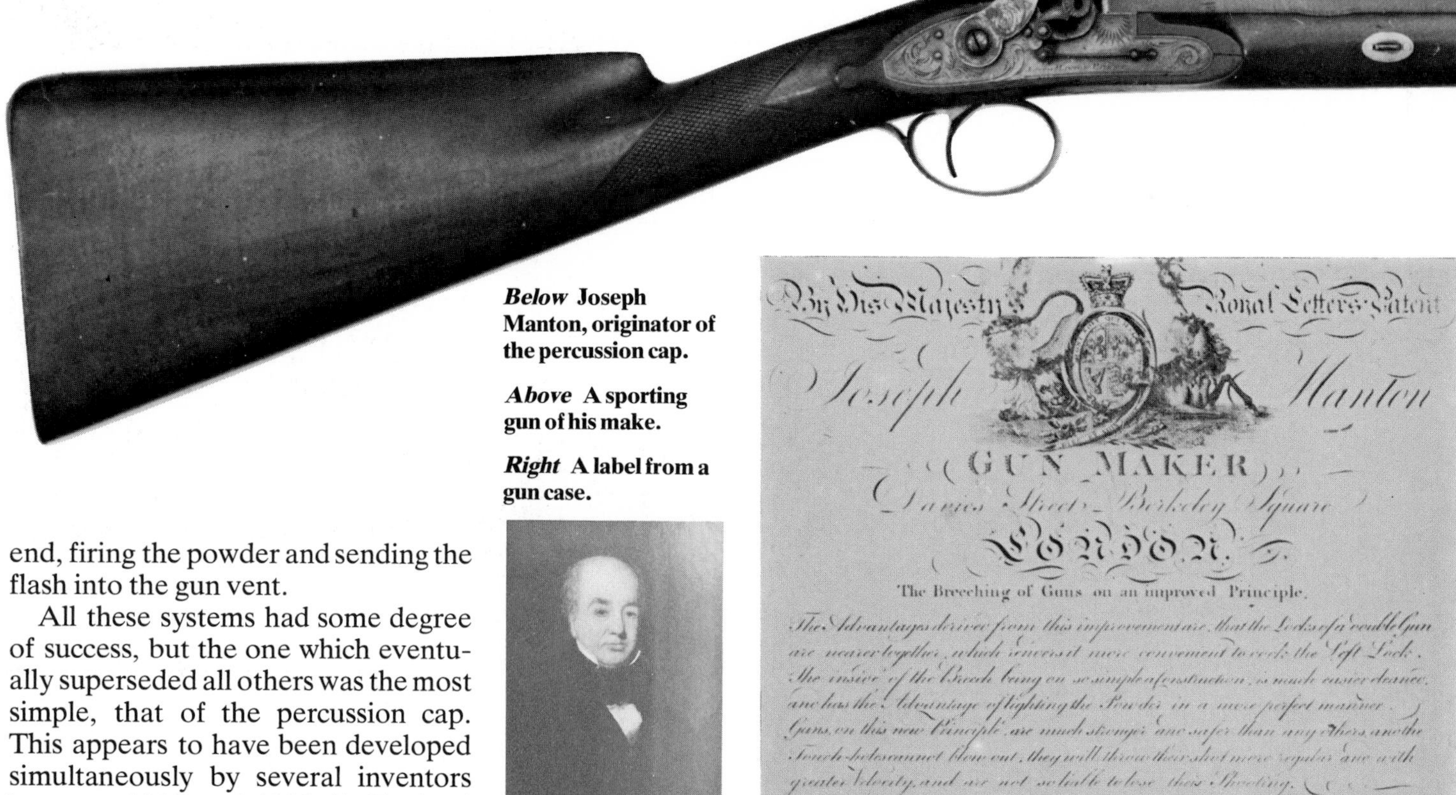

Below **Joseph Manton, originator of the percussion cap.**

Above **A sporting gun of his make.**

Right **A label from a gun case.**

end, firing the powder and sending the flash into the gun vent.

All these systems had some degree of success, but the one which eventually superseded all others was the most simple, that of the percussion cap. This appears to have been developed simultaneously by several inventors between 1818 and 1823. In England Joseph Manton and Joseph Egg perfected a system; in America Captain Joshua Shaw took out patents in 1822. The French gunsmith Prelat laid claim to the idea, as did Colonel Peter Hawker, a noted English sportsman. Whoever may have been first, the fact remains that in England Forsyth's patent of 1807 effectively prevented much progress prior to 1821.

After some false starts, the percussion cap settled down to a very simple pattern, that of a top hat of copper with a small coating of detonating powder inside the crown, secured there by a coat of varnish which also served to waterproof it. The gun vent now ended in an upturned 'nipple' with a central hole, upon which the cap was placed, open end down. The hammer fell, crushing the cap against the edges of the nipple and thus firing the detonating powder so as to send a powerful flash down the vent. A slight defect of the early caps was that, due to weak copper and strong powder, the caps frequently split, fragments flying off and endangering the firer. This was countered by making the hammer face hollow, so that at the moment of ignition the cap was entirely surrounded by steel. Another system adopted to guard against the disintegrating cap was to place the nipple below the breech and arrange the hammer to strike upwards, so that the body of the gun was between the cap and the firer's face. These 'underhammer' guns enjoyed some popularity and actually appeared as military weapons in Scandinavia.

As usual with a new idea, there was no rush by the military to adopt it overnight. By the early 1800s most nations had a sizeable amount of money invested in arms, and to scrap the lot and replace with something entirely new was an unpleasant prospect. Fortunately, the percussion system lent itself to conversion; it was relatively simple to remove the flintlock from a gun and replace it with a percussion lock.

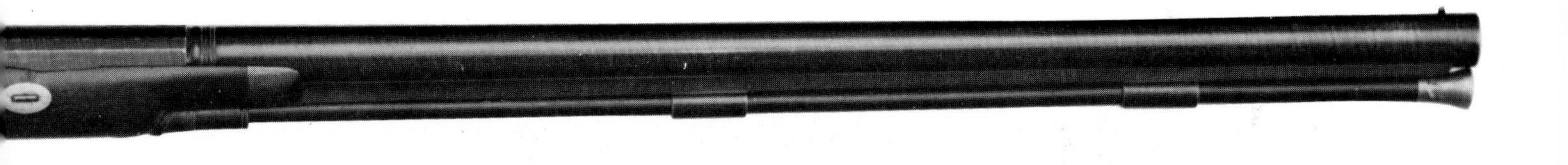

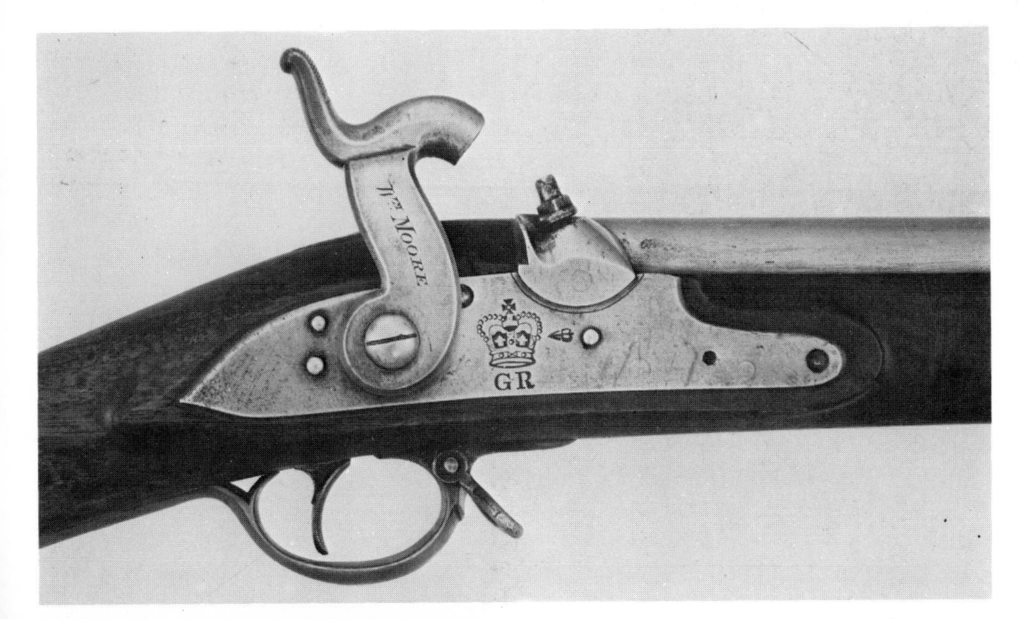

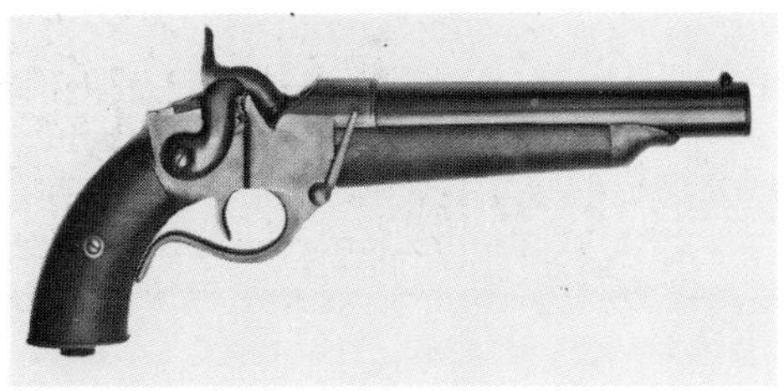

Above **An early breech-loading percussion pistol.**

Left **A percussion lock, c.1830.**

Below **A pair of decorated percussion duelling pistols.**

Below left **A pair of pocket pistols in mahogany case, fitted with Forsyth's patent sliding primers.**

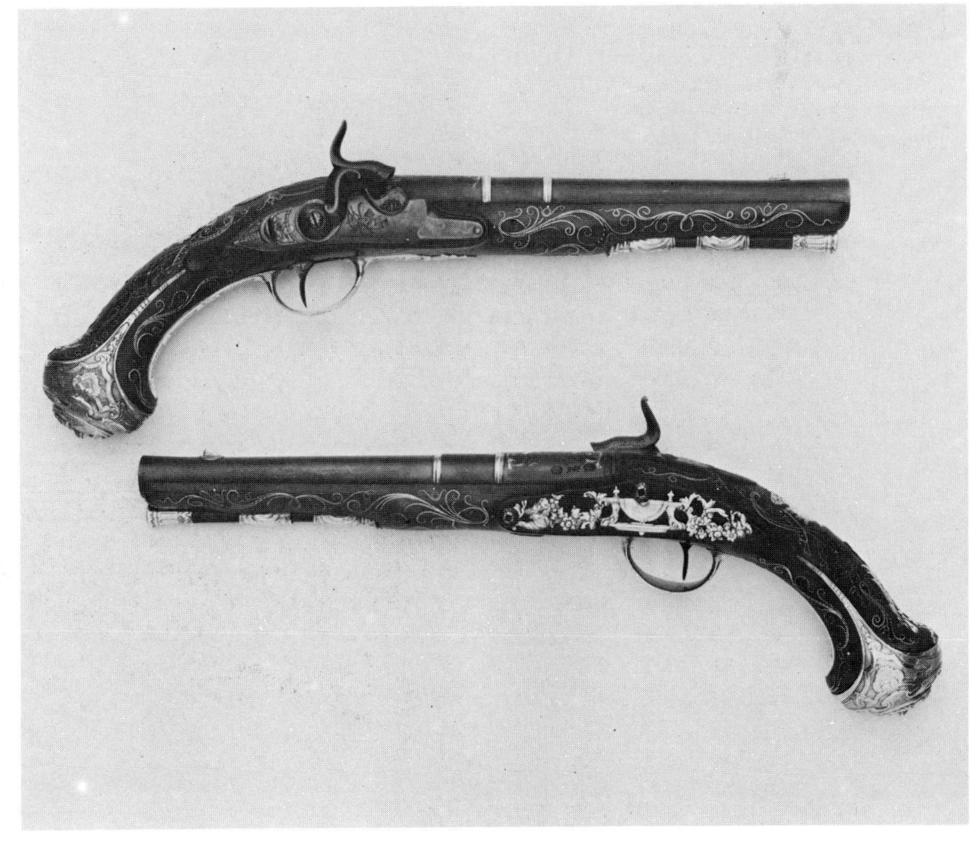

BREECH-LOADING FIREARMS

EARLY 19th CENTURY

THE INDUSTRIAL REVOLUTION brought about many changes, but one of the least-appreciated (or so it seems) was that it now became respectable to be an engineer, and the 19th century saw the engineer reach a status he never enjoyed before nor has done since. Consequently many intelligent and ingenious minds, which otherwise might not have contemplated mechanical problems, suddenly discovered innumerable technical problems waiting to be solved, with the added stimulus of a sizeable fortune for the best solution. And many of these minds began studying firearms and how to improve them.

One way to improve them, most people agreed, would be to load them from the breech end and do away with the prolonged performance with powder, ball and ramrod. There was nothing new in this idea, since breech loading firearms had been attempted right from the earliest days, particularly with cannon. But in those early days there was little real understanding of what went on inside the gun when it fired or of the type and magnitude of the pressures and temperatures involved. Moreover the ability to machine metal to fine limits on a production basis simply did not exist; it was one thing to spend months carefully hand-fitting a pistol for sale at a high price to a noble patron, but a totally different matter to attempt to duplicate it on a scale suitable to equipping an army.

Some of the earliest known breech-loading small arms are two carbines and two shield pistols made for Henry VIII. The carbines used a trap-door at the rear of the barrel which could be lifted and an iron tube, charged with powder and ball, inserted. Ignition was by wheel-lock through a vent incorporated in the tube. The shield pistols used a similar loading system but were matchlocks—and that itself is remarkable, for only one other specimen of a matchlock pistol is known. But in spite of excellent workmanship for their time, the sealing of the

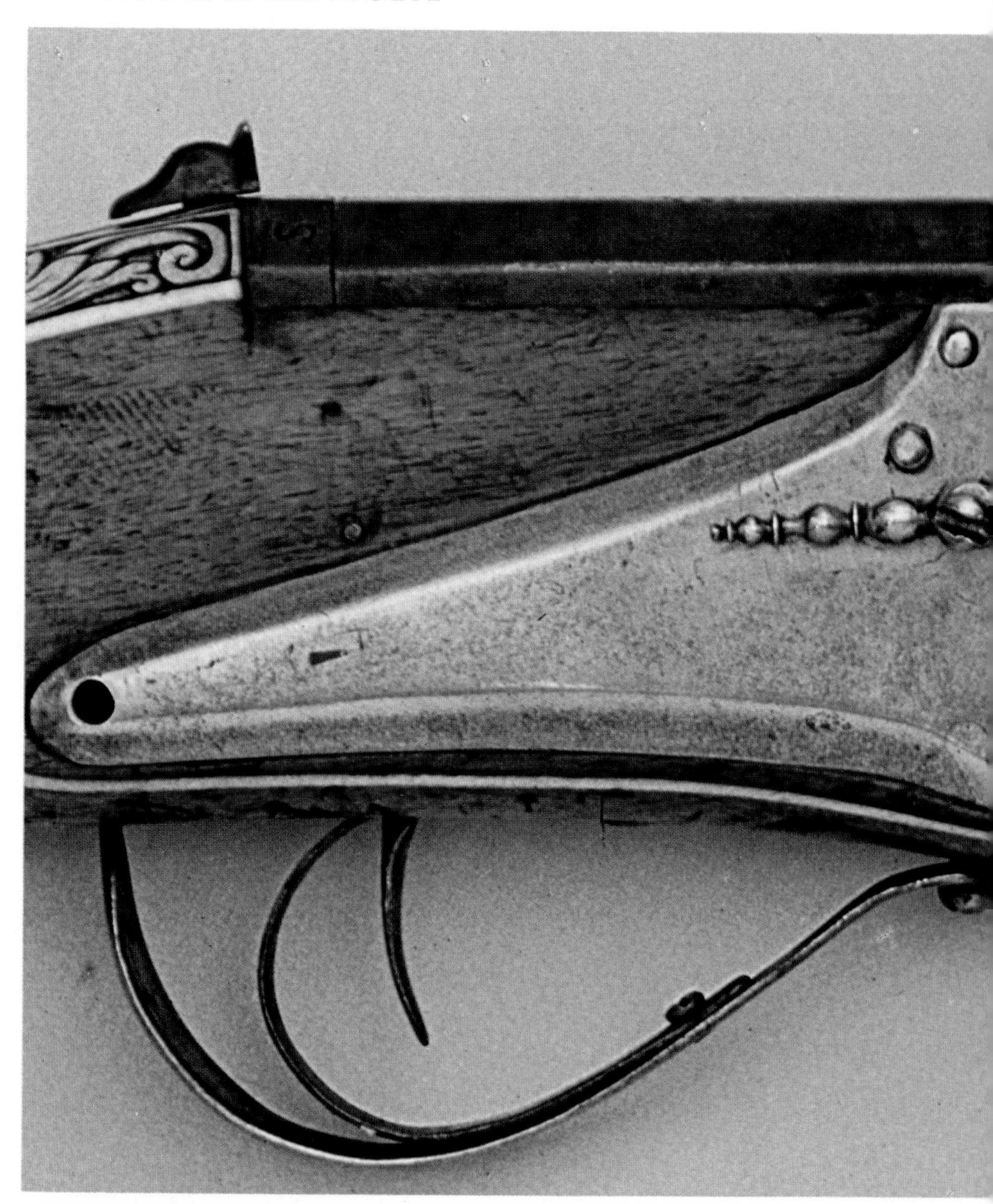

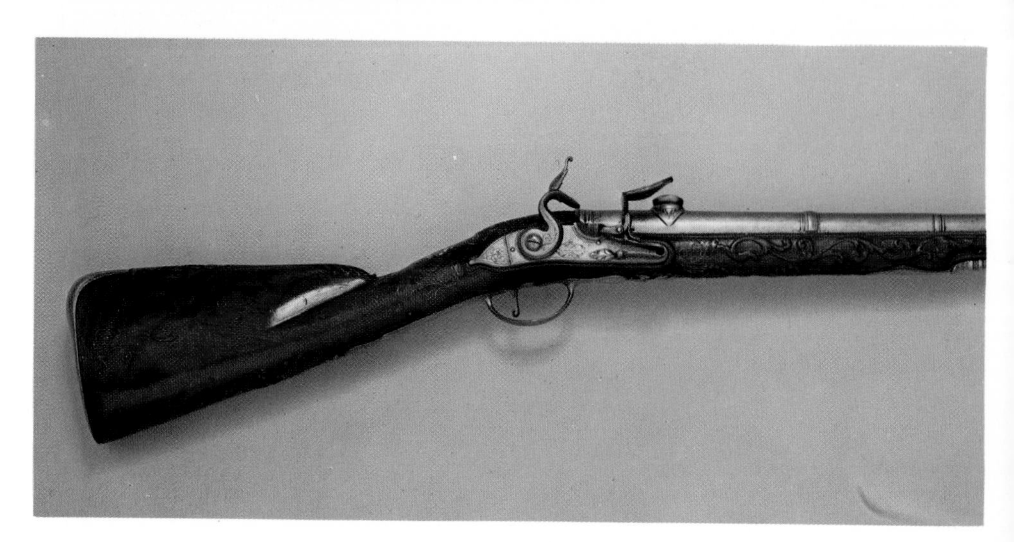

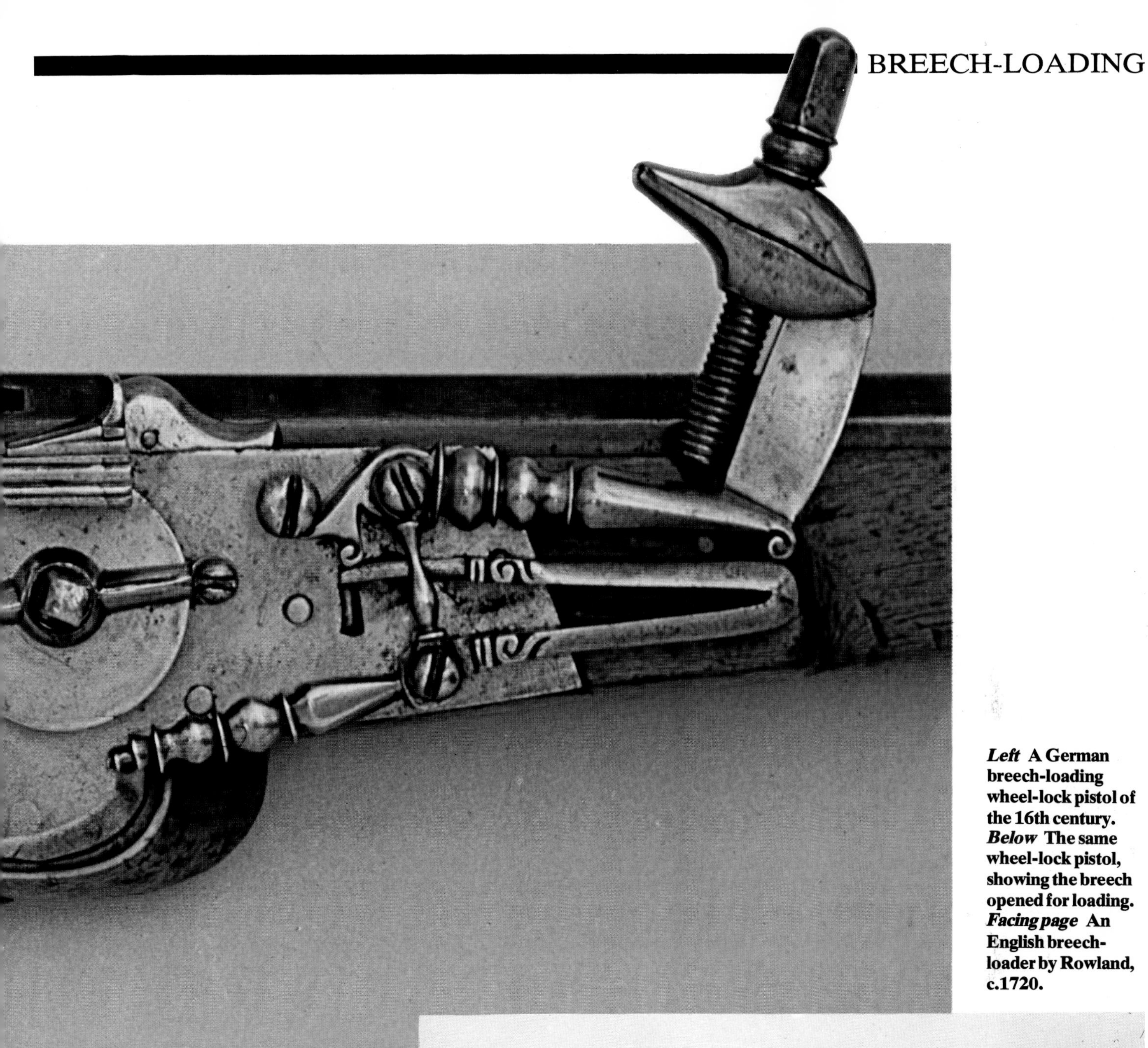

Left **A German breech-loading wheel-lock pistol of the 16th century.** ***Below*** **The same wheel-lock pistol, showing the breech opened for loading.** ***Facing page*** **An English breech-loader by Rowland, c.1720.**

breeches of these weapons left a lot to be desired.

The next attempt at breech-loading to amount to anything was an invention by de la Chaumette, a Frenchman; in 1704 he drilled a large vertical hole through the rear end of a musket barrel, cut a thread on it, and then closed the hole by a screwed plug inserted from below. The trigger guard formed a handle for the plug, and a few turns were sufficient to lower the top of the plug so that powder and ball could be inserted into the breech. The plug was then screwed up, and the gun was fired by the usual flintlock mechanism. Chaumette seems to have had relatively little success with the design, though some sporting guns were made on the principle, and it lay more or less neglected until revived and improved by Patrick Ferguson, a Scottish soldier, in the 1770s. Ferguson made the breech plug with a quick thread so that half-a-turn was enough to open the breech for loading; he also made the breech section of the plug with a smooth surface so that fouling could not jam the action, and he placed a greater thickness of metal below the breech to take the screw thread so that the plug could be lowered below the chamber level to facilitate cleaning the bore.

In 1776 Ferguson demonstrated his rifle in front of the Master General of the Ordnance. On a wet and windy day at Woolwich Marshes he fired his new gun at a steady rate of four or five shots a minute, and then capped this by walking towards the target, loading and firing as he went. As a result, one hundred 'Ferguson Rifles' were ordered to be made; a special 'Light Company' of 100 men was raised and, commanded by Ferguson and armed with the rifles, was sent to America. But the first major engagement of the Ferguson rifle was destined to be its last, though from no fault of the rifle. Ferguson and his light company were part of a diversionary attack at Brandywine Creek on 11 September 1777; they acquitted themselves with distinction until Ferguson was wounded by an American bullet. With the moving spirit removed, the light company was dispersed and the hundred rifles disappeared. Ferguson recovered from his wound, but before he could make a start in reforming the light company, he was killed at the Battle of King's Mountain, and the Ferguson rifle was never revived. The greatest mystery of all is what happened to his rifles? Only one or two of that original hundred are known to exist today, though others, made by gunsmiths for the Honourable East India Company and for private owners, have survived.

The first nation to adopt a breech-loader as standard was the United States when, in 1819, it began issuing the Hall Carbine. This had the rear

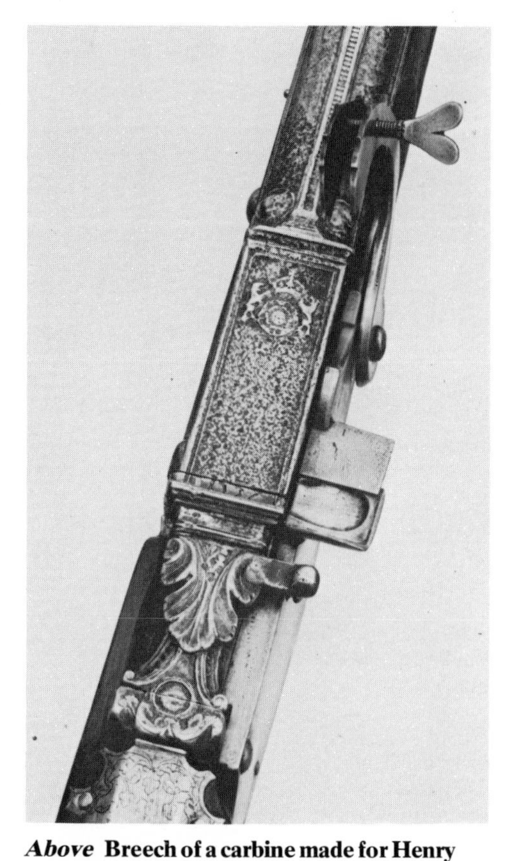

Above **Breech of a carbine made for Henry VIII, dated 1537.**
Below **A 'turn-off' pistol, breech-loaded by unscrewing the barrel.**

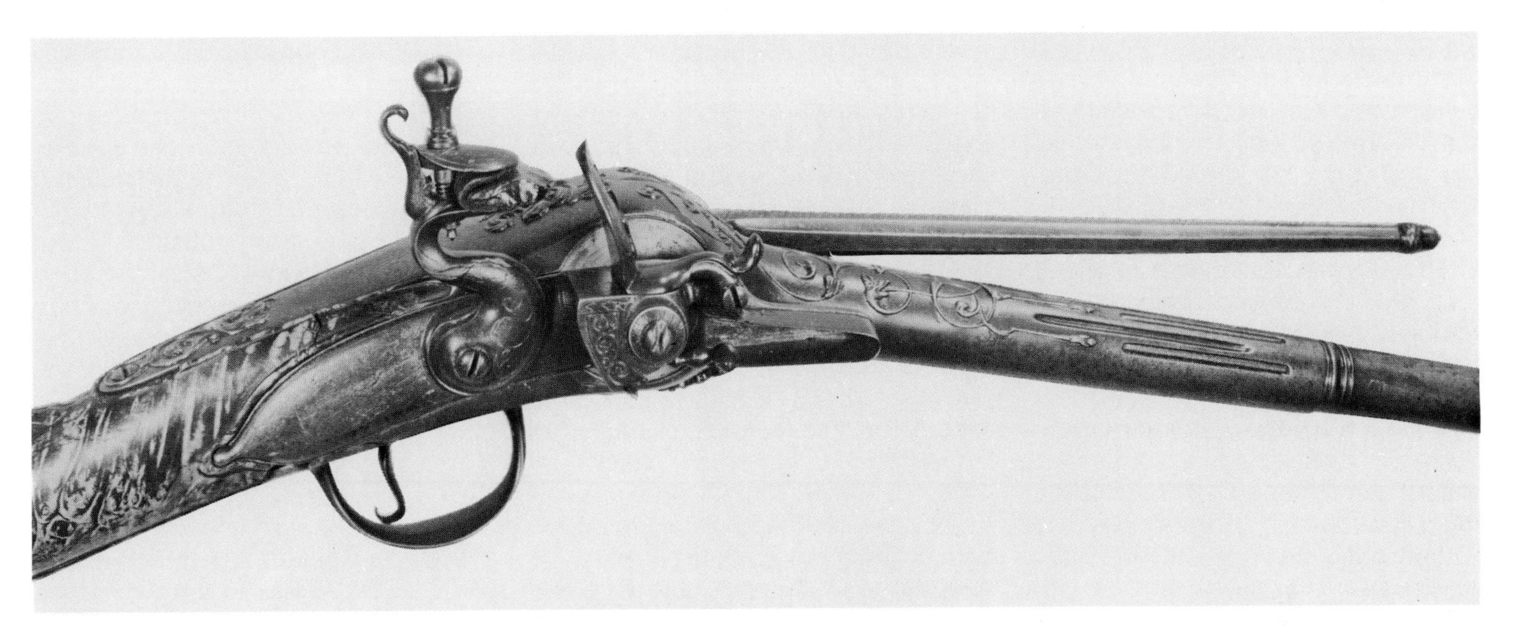

Above **A breech-loading magazine gun, c.1680.**

Right **The Hall breech-loading carbine, with removable breech and lock unit.**

A flintlock pistol with turn-off barrel and breech-loading, self-priming repeating action on the Lorenzoni system. The ball and powder are taken from the magazines in the butt (1) and transferred by gravity to the breech (2 and 3).

section of the barrel—the chamber—separated from the rest and hinged at the rear so that it could be tipped up and loaded. Ignition was by percussion, and the chamber section also carried the hammer and nipple, so that the loaded chamber could be withdrawn from the rifle and carried in the pocket to serve as an emergency pistol. Another innovative feature of the Hall carbine was that it was manufactured by machinery on an assembly-line principle, and the parts were interchangeable. It was far from perfect, for the joint between chamber and barrel soon began to leak due to the erosive effect of the hot gases, but it was to remain in service for almost fifty years.

It was the self-contained cartridge—i.e. a cartridge which held powder, bullet and means of ignition—which provided the complete answer to the breech-loading puzzle, and it was not until this apparently obvious point was appreciated that progress began to be made. The man who saw the cartridge as the key was a Swiss, Johannes Pauly.

Although Pauly's guns were greeted with acclaim by such figures as Napoleon and the Czar of Russia, they failed to achieve commercial success, and in 1814 he moved to London, where he died three years later.

THE REVOLVER

THROUGHOUT THE HISTORY of firearms there were periodic attempts to devise weapons which could be loaded with several charges and bullets and then discharged repeatedly without having to reload between shots.

One obvious system was to provide the gun with several barrels, firing them separately or collectively as the situation demanded. The 'Ducksfoot' pistol, with five or six splayed-out barrels was one solution and one which, it is said, was particularly popular with sailors on boarding a ship or confronting mutineers. Another famous weapon was Nock's Volley Gun, a seven-barrelled short musket produced for the Royal Navy in the 1780s. This consisted of a central barrel surrounded by a cluster of six more, all fired by a single flintlock mechanism. The lock fired the central chamber, from which ports communicating with the outer barrels fired the other six chambers simultaneously, which must have been something of a handful to control.

More practical was a gun firing one barrel at a time, and as early as the late 16th century there were examples of three-barrelled guns in which the group of barrels could be moved so as to bring each barrel into alignment with the matchlock in turn. In the 17th century came the idea of having one fixed barrel but placing a cylinder, containing a number of loaded chambers, behind it, discharging them one at a time through the barrel. The drawback here was the difficulty of arranging ignition; either a single pan and lock served each chamber in turn, having to be reprimed for each shot, or each chamber had its own loaded pan and frizzen; neither system was entirely satisfactory. Towards the end of the 18th century the 'Pepperbox' pistol became popular; this used a revolving cluster of barrels, fired by a flintlock, each barrel being hand-turned into alignment with the lock.

In 1818 Captain Artemus Wheeler of Concord, Massachusetts, obtained

a patent for a 'gun to discharge seven or more times', and this might be said to mark the birth of the revolver as we know it today. Wheeler's design was actually for a carbine or short musket, with a hand-revolved cylinder and flint ignition. It was examined by the U.S. Navy in 1821 but turned down. In the meanwhile, Wheeler's assistant, Elisha Collier, came to England and secured a patent for a 'firearm combining a single barrel with several chambers to obtain a succession of discharges from one loading.' Collier never denied that his inspiration came from Wheeler, but he incorporated some important features which lifted the design far beyond those which had preceded it. The most innovative feature was the provision of a spring to revolve the cylinder when the hammer was cocked. Another important feature was that the cylinder moved forward, under spring pressure, so that the rear end of the barrel entered into the mouth of the cylinder to form a close joint and so prevent the escape of flame and gas on firing. Other mechanical linkages were provided so as to lock the cylinder in place against the recoil force.

Altogether, the Collier pistol was a considerable advance, and although he failed to get it adopted as a military weapon (it was refused as being 'far too complicated and expensive to be applicable to the Public Service') the idea had some commercial success. Several English gunsmiths obtained licences from Collier to manufacture revolving pistols, shotguns and rifles to his patent. He then went into business as a gunsmith for a short time, but in 1827 he left the firearms field and turned to civil engineering for the remainder of his life.

It will be seen that the period of the Collier revolver spanned the time during which the percussion cap came into use, and his designs were accordingly changed in order to use this system of ignition, a far less involved matter than his original flintlock system. The percussion cap also revitalised the pepperbox revolver, and the 'bar-hammer' pepperbox, so called from the long hammer which stretched across the top of the pistol in order to reach the nipples on each barrel, became popular in England and America. The English designs were particularly important since they introduced trigger mechanisms which automatically rotated the barrel clus-

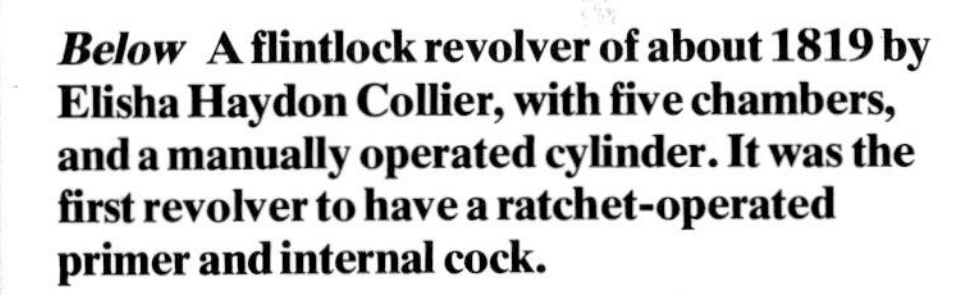

Below **A flintlock revolver of about 1819 by Elisha Haydon Collier, with five chambers, and a manually operated cylinder. It was the first revolver to have a ratchet-operated primer and internal cock.**

Left **Collier's second model of about 1820 with improvements, including an external cock and fluted cylinder.**

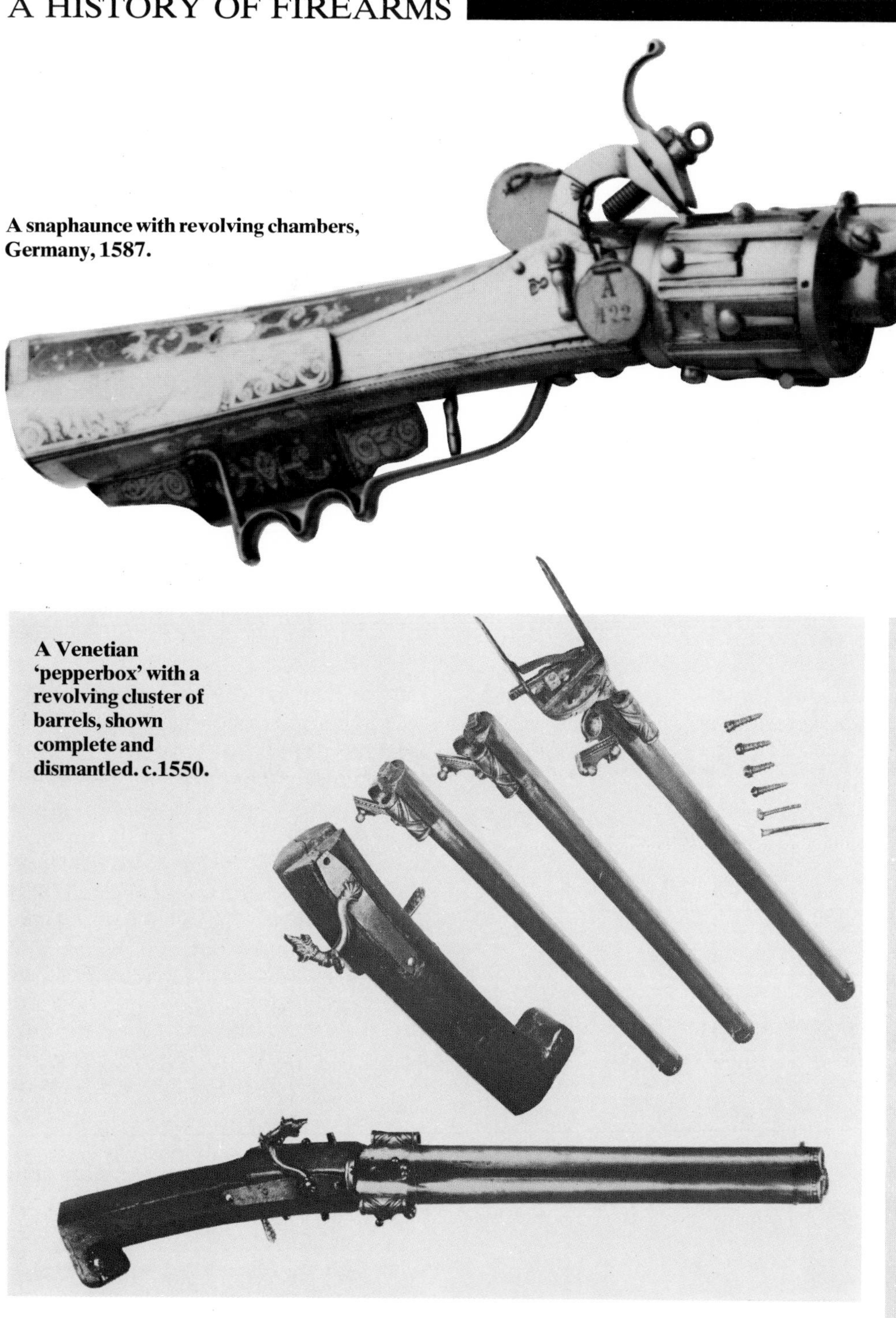

A snaphaunce with revolving chambers, Germany, 1587.

A Venetian 'pepperbox' with a revolving cluster of barrels, shown complete and dismantled. c.1550.

ter, locked it in place, and cocked and released the hammer all in one pull of the trigger, the so-called 'self-cocking' mechanism.

In spite of the efficiency of these arms, there was no great market for them. The London Proof House returns for the 1830–1850 period show that the average number of revolving arms submitted for proof (as they had to be before sale) was no more than about 300 a year. The revolver did not make a great appeal to the public until 1851, when the Great Exhibition was held in London and Samuel Colt displayed his wares to the public.

The career and pistols of Sam Colt are dealt with in greater detail in the body of the book, and will not, therefore, be repeated here. Suffice it to say that he had developed a percussion revolver and patented it in England in 1835 and in America in 1836. His patent was shrewdly drawn and effectively blocked any competitive development of a revolver with a mechanically-rotated cylinder in America until it expired in 1857. The English patent was never actively worked in England, and it is doubtful

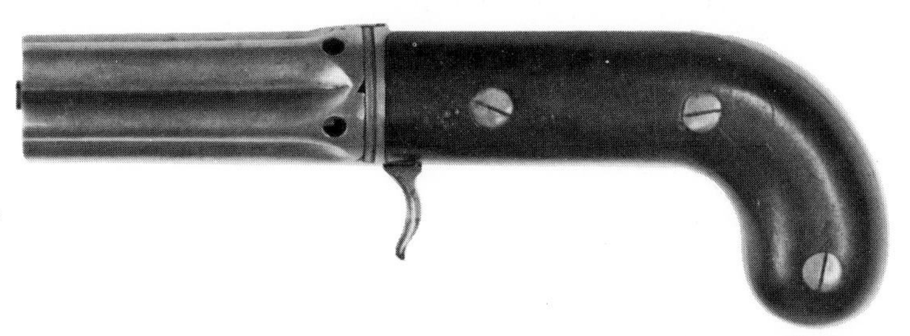

Left **An English five-shot pepperbox pistol by Budding of Stroud.**

Below **The 'Defence' revolver invented by James Puckle (left) showing the square chambered cylinder for 'use against infidels'.** ***Inset*** **A printed patent for the 'Defence' revolver.**

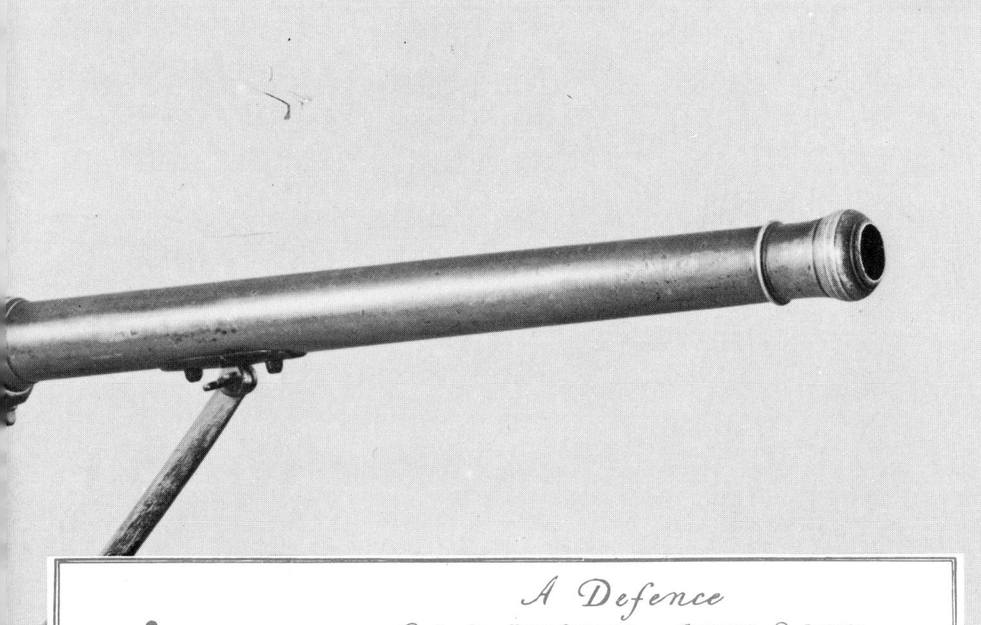

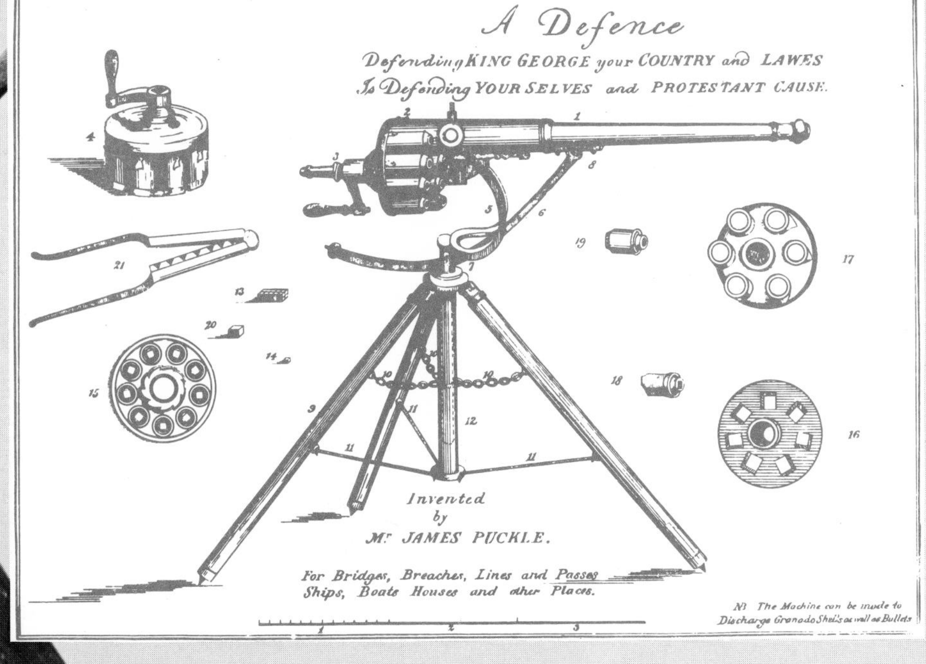

whether his claims would have withstood too close an examination; the existence of mechanically-rotated cylinders on pepperbox revolvers prior to 1836 would probably have invalidated much of his claim. But in any event, as we have already said, there was little public interest in revolvers in England.

After going into liquidation with his first revolver venture, Colt was given a second chance by the advent of the Mexican War of 1847, and from then on, aided by the 1849 Gold Rush, his company prospered. In 1851 his exhibits in London attracted enormous interest, which he carefully fostered by a variety of astute publicity stunts, and suddenly the western world began to clamour for revolvers.

Colt's revolvers were of the 'open frame' pattern; the butt frame carried the hammer and cylinder, and the barrel was affixed to the front of this frame by a removable key. Thus, there was no connection between the barrel and the upper portion of the frame and the top surface of the cylinder was exposed. By knocking out the key, the barrel could be removed, followed by the cylinder, for cleaning, after which the cylinder could be loaded with powder and ball or with prepared paper cartridges, caps placed on the nipples, and the gun re-assembled. To simplify re-loading, Colt later developed a lever-rammer which lay beneath the barrel and could be unclipped to allow the chambers to be reloaded without having to dismantle the weapon completely.

At the 1851 Exhibition, Colt's only serious competitor was Robert Adams of London. Adams had developed the 'solid frame' revolver in which the butt frame and barrel were forged as a single piece of metal, a rectangle being left in the frame into which the cylinder was fitted. This resulted in a much stronger form of construction. Adams also used a different firing mechanism to that of Colt. The Colt was a 'single action' pistol in which the hammer had to be manually cocked for each shot, being released by pressure on the trigger. The Adams was a 'self-cocking' pistol in which pulling the trigger lifted and dropped the hammer. Both systems have their advantages; the single action was better for accuracy, since the relatively light pull needed to release the cocked hammer was unlikely to upset the aim. The self-cocking lock, however, demanded a much greater effort to pull through on the trigger, and this invariably caused the pistol to waver off its aim. On the other hand, for rapid fire in action, the self-cocking lock was preferred since the firer merely kept on pulling the trigger.

Both Colt and Adams competed for military contracts, and Colt was, due to the better accuracy stemming from the single-action lock, fortunate in securing a contract to provide revolvers to the British Army and Navy. But the Crimean War showed the advantages of the Adams design in close combat, and when Lieut. Beaumont made an improvement to Adams' lock which allowed the user to select either single action or self-cocking action — the 'double-action' lock — the Adams supplanted the Colt in British service.

With the advent of metallic cartridges the revolver designers now had to devise methods of loading and unloading at the rear of the cylinder, and this led to a plethora of patented contraptions. Eventually three systems outlived the rest: gate-loading, in which the cartridges were inserted one at a time into the chambers, through a

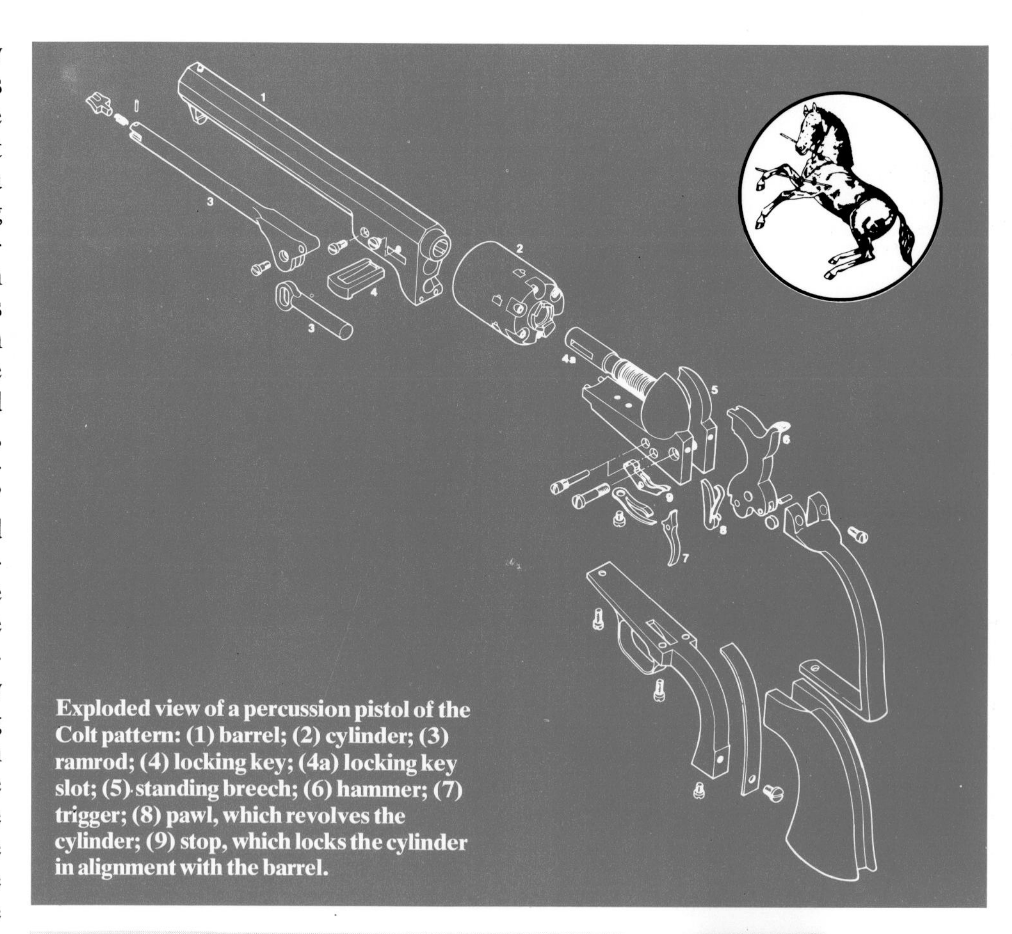

Exploded view of a percussion pistol of the Colt pattern: (1) barrel; (2) cylinder; (3) ramrod; (4) locking key; (4a) locking key slot; (5) standing breech; (6) hammer; (7) trigger; (8) pawl, which revolves the cylinder; (9) stop, which locks the cylinder in alignment with the barrel.

Above **A typical Adams solid-frame ·45 revolver of 1872.**

Right **The English gunsmith Robert Adams loading the revolver of HRH the Prince Consort.**

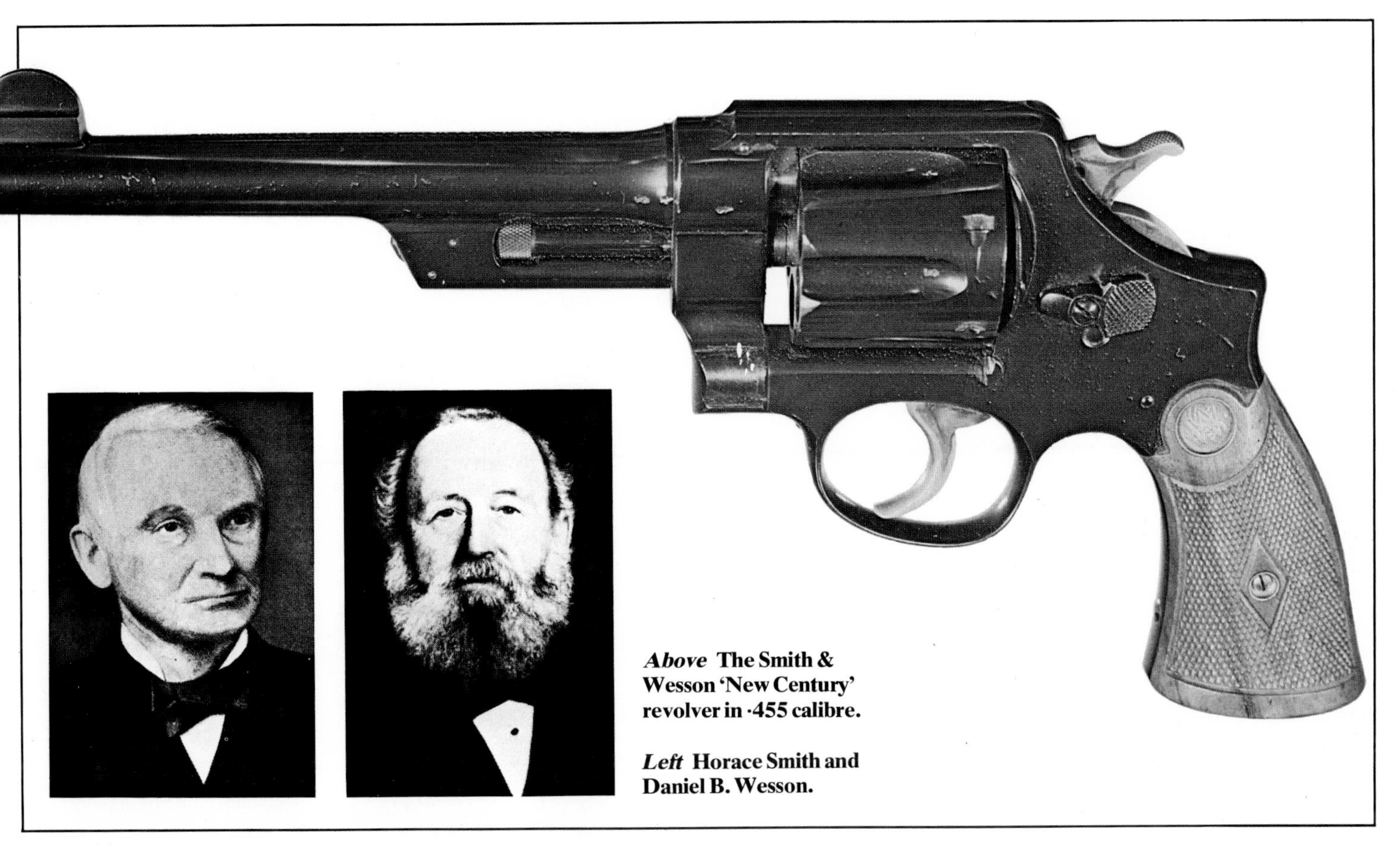

Above **The Smith & Wesson 'New Century' revolver in ·455 calibre.**

Left **Horace Smith and Daniel B. Wesson.**

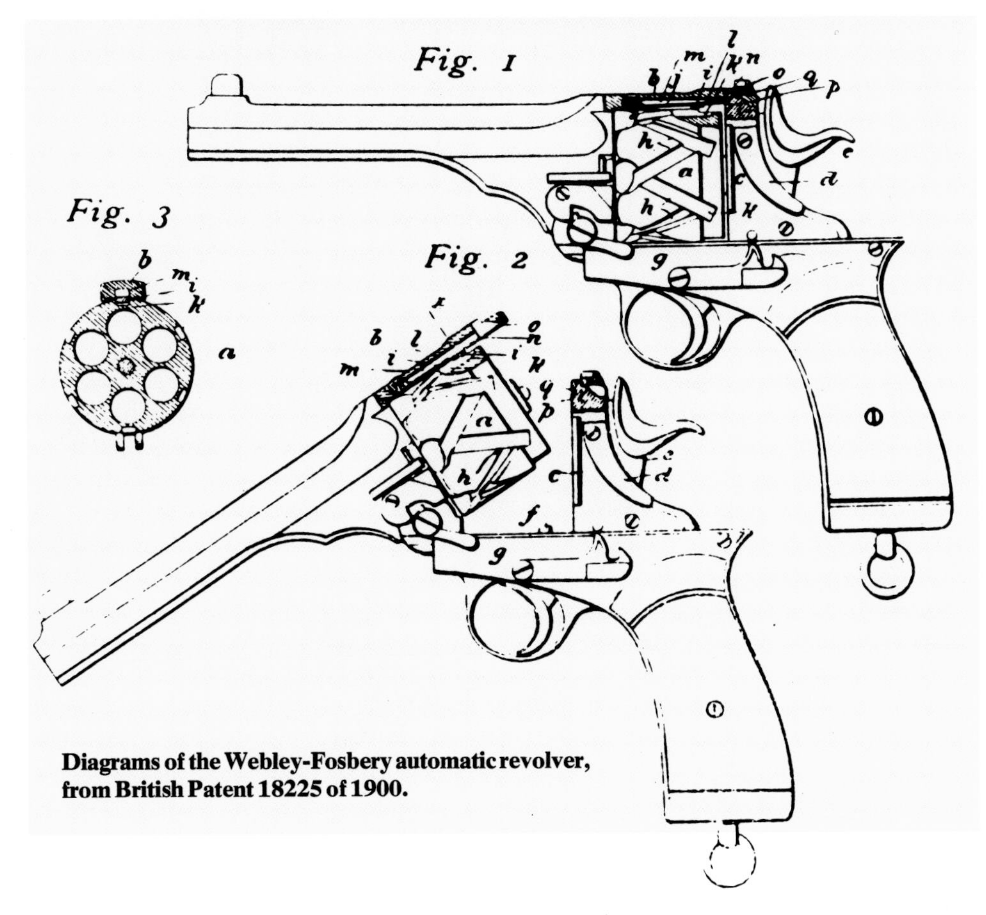

Diagrams of the Webley-Fosbery automatic revolver, from British Patent 18225 of 1900.

gate or trap at the side of the breech; the hinged frame, in which the barrel and cylinder swung away from the frame to expose the rear face of the cylinder; and the side-opening solid frame revolver in which the cylinder was carried on a 'crane arm' and could be swung out to lie alongside the frame for loading. Extraction of the empty cases was achieved in the first case by a rod beneath the barrel which, thrust backwards, pushed the spent cases through the gate one by one, and in the other two cases by arranging a plate in the centre of the cylinder to move outward, catching beneath the cartridge case rims and thus ejecting them.

Except for aberrant forms such as the Webley-Fosbery automatic revolver, the Landstadt and the Dardick revolvers, the basic pattern for revolvers was settled by the early 1890s and development since then has largely been in matters of detail or improved systems of manufacture.

THE RIFLE

THE FACT THAT A spinning bullet could be made to fly more accurately than one fired from a smoothbored barrel seems to have been discovered some time late in the 15th century, but where and by whom is another unsolved mystery. The earliest known rifled arm is a matchlock hunting rifle owned by the Emperor Maximilian in 1500. Many hypotheses have been advanced to account for the development of rifling, but we can only continue to speculate. The most likely theory is that archers were accustomed to cant the feathers on their arrows in order to achieve some degree of spin (more probably, roll stabilisation), finding (probably by accident) that this improved the accuracy of flight, and thus the development of rifling in firearms was a logical follow-on. This is probably true; what is quite certain is that it was two or three hundred years before there was any sort of understanding of why rifled arms shot more accurately.

But even if the theory was absent, practical results spoke loud enough, and from the 16th century onwards, rifled arms were made. Not in great numbers, since rifling was a long and difficult—and hence costly—process, so that rifles were originally the property of wealthy hunters and sportsmen. Moreover the owners had to take some pains with their ammunition, casting their own bullets very precisely to ensure that they would fit the rifling grooves correctly, for the bullet which was too loose a fit was of little or no use. This, of course, led to problems after a few shots had been fired; the fouling set up by the residue from the burned gunpowder charge made it harder and harder to force the

Top **The Snider breech-loading conversion of a British service rifle.**

Bottom **The Martini-Henry rifle, with action open to allow a cartridge to be inserted across the top of the breech block.**

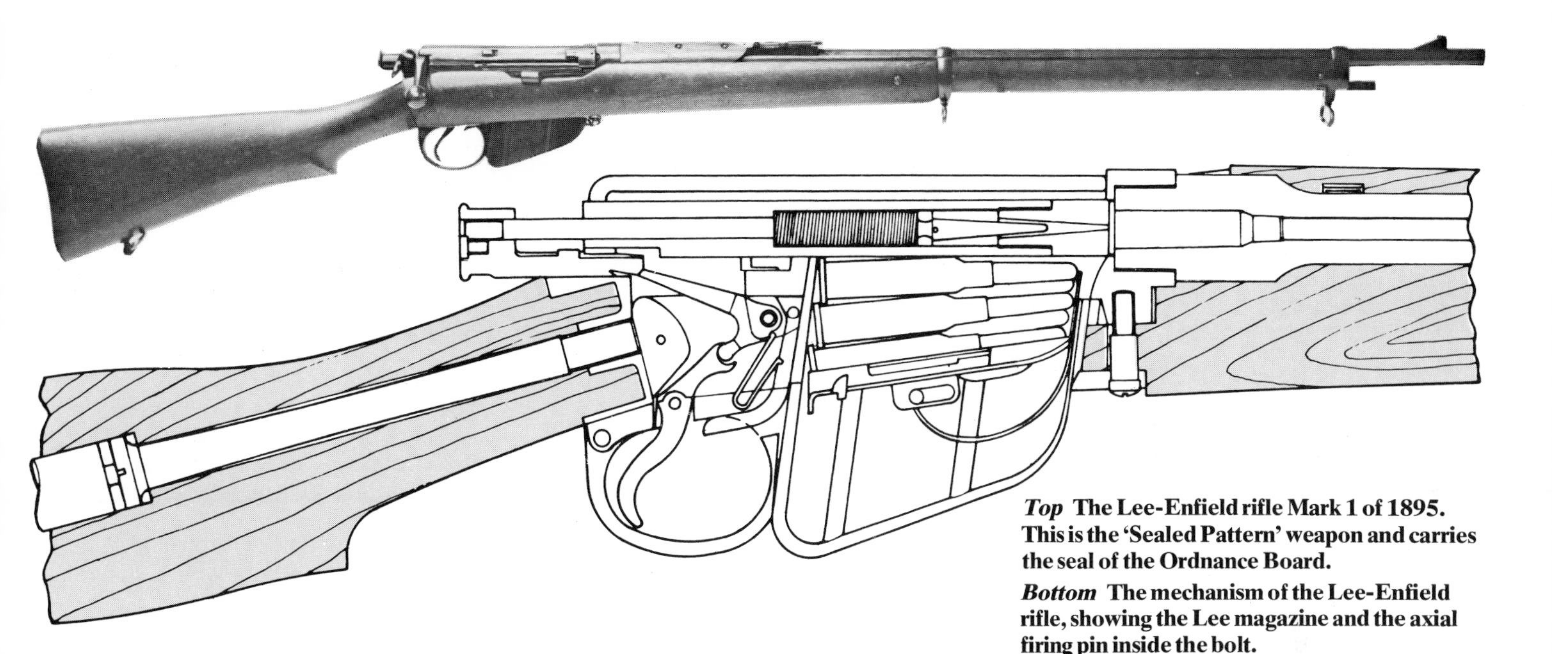

Top **The Lee-Enfield rifle Mark 1 of 1895. This is the 'Sealed Pattern' weapon and carries the seal of the Ordnance Board.**

Bottom **The mechanism of the Lee-Enfield rifle, showing the Lee magazine and the axial firing pin inside the bolt.**

ball down the barrel, and the bullet generally had to be 'started' in the muzzle by a wooden mallet. Eventually, the shooter had no alternative but to stop firing and thoroughly clean the barrel before he could continue.

Very soon it was found that a simpler way was to 'patch' the bullet; to enclose it in a cloth or thin leather wad which had been greased. The ball used with this system was of smaller calibre than the barrel and thus ball and patch could be easily rammed down. On firing, the patch would 'set up' and fill the rifling grooves behind the bullet, grip the ball and impart the desired spin, and then fall clear as it left the muzzle. This also helped to reduce the fouling, since the grease left in the bore softened the powder residue and the wad swept the grooves clean with each shot.

In spite of the extra expense involved in rifling a weapon, it was soon appreciated that in the hands of trained men a few rifles could be most effective in battle, and rifles began to appear in military service in the 17th century. King Christian IV of Denmark is generally credited with being the first to put the rifle into military service but he was soon followed by others. In some armies the would-be rifleman was required to provide his own rifle, on the assumption that he would probably produce a better weapon than the military could afford and also that he would already be familiar with it and thus require little or no further training.

We have already discussed the Ferguson rifle when dealing with breech-loading, since it was the breech arrangement which made the Ferguson unique in its period. In America, had it survived, it would have been pitted against the legendary 'Kentucky Rifle'. The rifle had gone to America in the early years of the 18th century, as Swiss, German and Bohemian gunsmiths emigrated to the New World and set up in business, and that business became largely the making of hunting rifles. These were, at first, heavy weapons with 7-grooved rifling in large calibre barrels—calibres of ·5 to ·7 of an inch were usual. Such weapons had answered well in European hunting, but conditions in America were somewhat different; a hunting trip was not an afternoon's walk in the woods but a protracted and strenuous expedition, and the hunters wanted lighter rifles. Moreover, they argued, a smaller calibre would kill game just as well and economise on

THE TARGET RIFLE

Competitive rifle shooting doubtless began with a simple contest between two men as to who could shoot straightest, but over the years it has become an extremely involved and compartmented occupation. There are contests for military rifles, single shot rifles, automatic rifles, contests in which the rifle must be held to the shoulder, in which it may be partially supported, and in which it is entirely rested on a bench; with open sights and with telescopes; in the condition it left the makers' hands and with every modification which the owner can contrive. The present-day match rifle, as illustrated here, has become a high-precision machine for punching holes in targets and wholly impractical for anything else. The stock is carefully tailored to the individual so that he always holds it in precisely the same fashion; the trigger is adjustable for strength of pull; the sights compensate for drift, wind and, jump while the rifling and the barrel are prepared with surgical precision. The result is as accurate and consistent a firearm as it is possible to make.

Above **A Japanese 38th Year Carbine, designed by Arisaka.**
Right **The Mauser bolt-action rifle of 1871.**
Below right **The Chassepot rifle with bolt open for loading.**
Below **An American Sharps carbine.**

lead. And so the American rifle evolved; a thinner and longer barrel of about ·45 inch calibre with a maple-wood stock and with a unique 'patch box' incorporated in the butt for spare flints and bullet patches.

The majority of the gunsmiths specialising in these weapons settled in Pennsylvania, and the rifle is more properly known as the 'Pennsylvania Rifle'. Today they are more often, and incorrectly, called 'Kentucky' rifles due to a popular ballad from the War of 1812 which sang of Andrew Jackson's 'Kentucky Mountain Men' and their rifles at the Battle of New Orleans. The accuracy of these rifles was legendary; one contemporary report speaks of putting eight consecutive shots into a 5 inch by 7 inch target at sixty yards' range, while a British officer who frequently found himself on the wrong end of these rifles gave his opinion that the average American marksman could hit an enemy in the head at 200 yards.

The principal drawback with the rifle as a military weapon was the slowness of loading, even with prepared cartridges. The patch had to be put across the muzzle and the ball started truly down the bore and rammed. As a result, military riflemen were often accompanied by other soldiers armed with muskets so as to be able to produce some improved firepower in the event of a counter-attack against the rifleman. The only answer to this would be to produce a bullet which would be of such small diameter that it would pass easily down the bore during loading but which would, by some means, expand to fit tightly into the rifling grooves.

In the 1840s a Frenchman, Thouve-

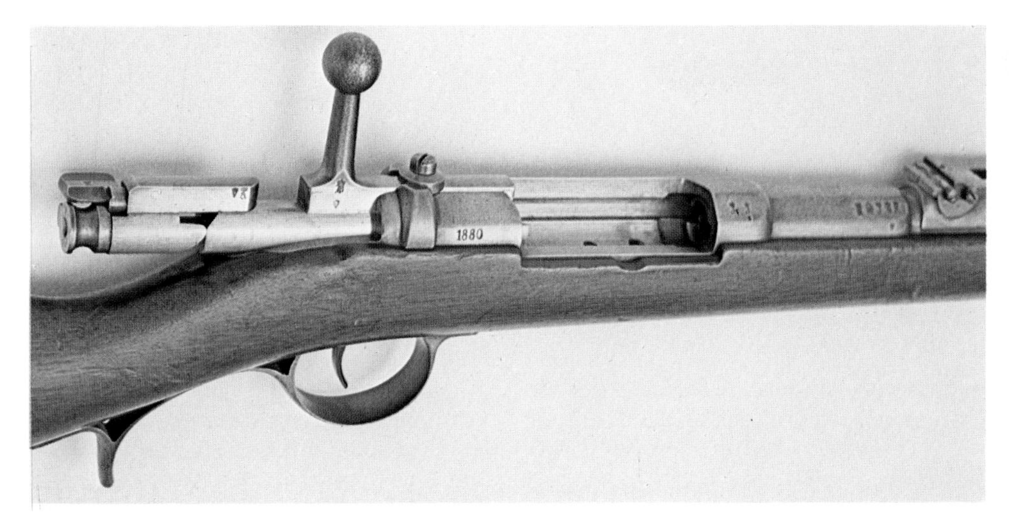

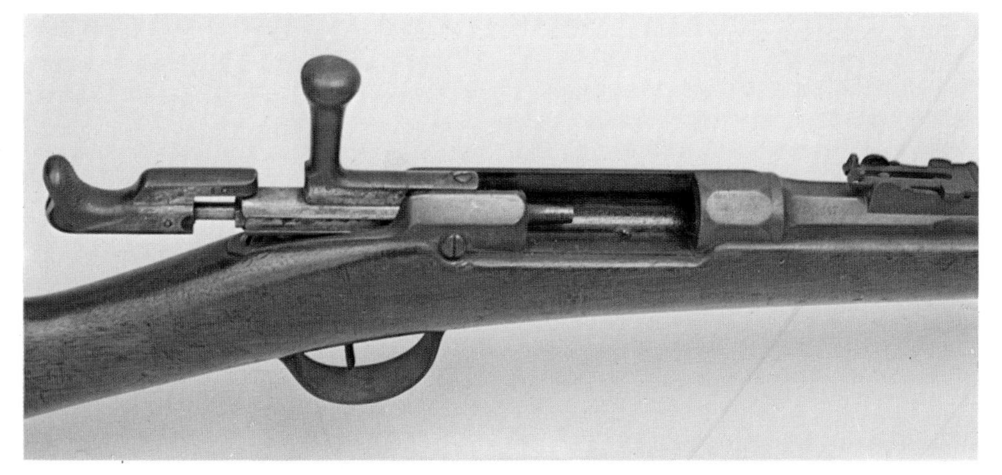

nin, developed a pointed cylindrical bullet which was used in a special gun which carried a pillar in the centre of the chamber. The powder was loaded first and occupied the space around the pillar; the bullet was then dropped down the barrel so that its base rested on the tip of the pillar, whereupon a few sharp blows with the ramrod deformed the base of the bullet so that it spread out by impact on the pillar and expanded into the rifling.

This worked, but the deformation of the bullet was rather hit-and-miss and the pounding of the rammer upset the head shape resulting in irregular flight. A better solution was to hollow out the base of the bullet and allow the explosion of the charge to expand the 'skirt' of the bullet into the rifling. This system was first proposed by William Greener, an English gunsmith, in 1835, but in spite of demonstrations the idea did not catch on. In 1846 Captain Minie, a French officer, developed a pointed bullet with a hollow base, and with a small iron cup in the base, which under pressure forced out the lower edge of the bullet into the rifling. The 'Minie bullet', with various minor improvements, became the standard rifle bullet for the remainder of the muzzle-loading era.

Although the usual form of rifling is the 'polygroove' system in which a number of spiral grooves are cut into the barrel, there have been other ways of spinning the bullet and it is worth considering some of them, even if only to illustrate the boundless ingenuity of gun designers.

The Brunswick rifle, adopted in British service in 1835, had only two grooves, opposite each other and unusually deep. The bullet was a ball with a central raised belt which engaged with the grooves as the bullet was loaded and which imparted the spin as it was ejected. In theory it was a sound enough system, but the effect of the raised belt on the bullet's flight was such that it was impossible to hit anything at ranges greater than 400 yards.

Another idea, developed first in Denmark and later enthusiastically promoted in England by Lancaster, was to make the gun's bore oval instead of circular, and then develop it into a twist. An oval bullet was used and this, following the twisted bore, developed the necessary spin.

A similar idea was the Whitworth Hexagonal Bore in which the rifle barrel was a twisted hexagon in section, with the bullets shaped to suit.

With the arrival of breech loading most of the aberrant forms of rifling disappeared; most of them had been concerned with reducing the problems raised by powder fouling, and once it became practical to clean a rifle by passing a brush completely through the barrel, such problems diminished. Simple polygroove rifling became the standard pattern and has remained so.

THE MACHINE GUN

THERE HAS ALWAYS been a desire to increase the firepower of an army without increasing the number of soldiers to be clothed and fed, and this tendency can be discerned from the earliest times. In the 15th century the 'ribauldequin' was developed, a light two-wheeled cart carrying several small-calibre cannon barrels which could be touched off in a ragged volley to deliver a blast of shot. In 1718 James Puckle produced his 'defence' gun, a tripod-mounted revolver which allowed a rapid fire to be put down. Two cylinders were provided, one to fire round bullets against Christians, and one chambered for square bullets to be fired against infidels. A handful were made, two of which now remain, but Puckle's company went bankrupt and the idea fell by the wayside.

In 1851 a Belgian, Captain Fafschamps, invented a multiple-barrelled gun in which a cluster of barrels were enclosed in a cylindrical casing so that it resembled a cannon. A plate carrying a number of cartridges could be placed behind these barrels and clamped in position and the cartridges fired in succession through the barrels. He passed the idea to a manufacturer named Montigny who perfected it, and it was then adopted, in great secrecy, by the French Army as the 'Mitrailleuse' or 'grape-shot shooter'. Mechanically the idea was sound enough, but during the Franco-Prussian War it was tactically mishandled, which set the mitrailleuse idea back several years in military eyes.

It was the American Civil War which had given the machine gun its start. The first attempts were a reversion to the 'ribauldequin' or 'organ gun' idea, a collection of 25 rifle barrels on a wheeled carriage. Each barrel had to be muzzle-loaded, after which a priming of gunpowder was run across the 25 vents and ignited by a percussion cap and hammer. The result was a formidable volley, but this was followed by a long pause for reloading, so the 'Billinghurst-Requa

A contemporary engraving of the Montigny Mitrailleuse, or 'grape-shot shooter'.

Battery Gun' found very few supporters among the military.

Somewhat more practical was the 'Ager Coffee Mill', which used a single breech-loaded barrel. Steel tubes were pre-loaded with powder and ball and had a percussion cap affixed to a nipple at the rear end, after which they were dropped into a hopper on top of the gun. Turning a hand crank fed the tubes one at a time into the breech, dropped a hammer on to the cap, and then extracted the fired tube; the gunner and his mate then had the job of picking up the empty tubes, cleaning them and re-loading them before the next engagement.

The most famous of the mechanical guns which appeared at this period was, of course, the Gatling Gun. Gatling appears to have appreciated the problem which had been pointed out by military critics of the Ager Gun; that firing a hundred shots a minute—or, as one commentator put it, '7500 grains of powder and seven pounds of lead every minute'—would raise the barrel to a very high temperature. To get round this, and also to simplify the mechanical problems of feeding and extracting at a high rate of fire, Gatling built his gun with six barrels which revolved. As any one barrel was at the topmost position, a cartridge was dropped behind the chamber, and as it travelled downwards this cartridge was gradually chambered and the breech closed, until at the bottom-most point on its travel that barrel was fired. As it now moved up so the breech was opened and the fired case extracted, so that as it reached the top it was ready for another cartridge. In this way if the gun fired at, say, 600 rounds a minute, any one barrel fired at only 100 rounds a minute and spent the rest of its time travelling around to cool down.

In spite of inventing the gun during the Civil War, Gatling sold very few, largely because his political sympathies were suspected and because his factory was in Cincinnati, Ohio; it was thought that if he were given a contract to make guns for the Union Army, the Confederates might very easily promote a raid across the Ohio river and seize the shipment just as it was completed. After the war, though, the US Army and Navy both adopted the gun, and it was widely sold to Britain, France, Russia and many other countries.

Other mechanical machine guns which appeared in the 1870s were the Lowell, Gardner and Nordenfelt, all of which will be found in the Encyclopedia pages. Although the mechanical principle was superseded by the 1880s, the mechanical guns lingered into the early years of the 20th century before being scrapped. But the basic attraction of the Gatling—the division of work among a cluster of barrels—remained, and in the 1940s the idea was revived in order to produce a high-speed gun for aircraft use. When two fighter aircraft are dog-fighting or a single machine is attempting to fire at a ground target, the period of time during which gun and target are aligned gets shorter and shorter as the aircraft gets faster and faster. With the speeds that jet aircraft were reaching the engagement time had dropped to about one second, and the contemporary machine guns, which in one second could fire only six or seven shots, were no longer effective. The Gatling, driven by an electric motor instead of a hand crank, could deliver up to 6000 shots a minute, 100 shots a second, and could thus produce a worthwhile volume of fire in a brief period of time. This line of thought led to the 20mm Vulcan cannon, and eventually to guns in rifle calibres.

But in the 1870s the only power available was manpower, or so it seemed. Then came Hiram Maxim, who brought an enquiring and inventive mind of the first order to bear on the problem and who rapidly realised that the recoil of the gun, which was usually cursed as a useless and unfortunate byproduct, was a source of untapped energy. By treating the recoil force as a source of power and using it to drive the gun mechanism, it would thus be possible to make an 'automatic' machine gun, one which would continue to fire of its own volition so long as somebody held down the trigger and supplied it with ammunition.

Two sailors operating a Gardner machine gun.

Broadly speaking, there are two ways of driving an automatic weapon, be it machine gun, rifle or pistol: by means of the recoil force or the pressure of gas inside the barrel which is generated by the explosion of the cartridge. Within these two broad categories there are an infinite number of sub-divisions, though only a few of them will produce a practical weapon. The principal sub-division is whether or not the breech block is securely locked to the barrel when the gun is fired. With a low-powered cartridge in a short barrel there is no need to lock the breech; the inertia of the breech block is sufficient to resist the

Left **An artist's impression of a Gatling-equipped 'camel corps'. The latter was intended to publicise a compact, short-barreled version known as the Camel Gun and there is little evidence to suggest that such a corps ever existed.**
Above **The manufacturer's nameplate on the breech of the Rotunda Gatling.**
Below **Richard Jordan Gatling (1818–1903), inventor of the first successful 'mechanical' machine gun.**

opening force due to pressure on the back of the cartridge case, at least long enough to allow the bullet to leave the barrel and the chamber pressure to drop. Where more powerful cartridges are used, as, for example, in most military machine guns, it is necessary to lock the breech block since the longer barrel and heavier bullet mean that the pressure is retained longer and an unsupported breech would begin to open while the pressure was dangerously high. When this occurs, the cartridge case is ejected violently and, due to the pressure inside, usually bursts as it leaves the chamber. In other cases the interior pressure expands the mouth of the case so tightly that it refuses to move when the base of the case begins to leave the chamber and the case therefore splits in the middle. Either way, the result is not conducive to safety or to reliable operation.

Study of patents files shows that several inventors have realised the potentialities of gas and recoil but they were beaten before they began until the self-contained metallic cartridge was perfected. So long as a cartridge consisted of a handful of powder, a lead ball and a piece of flint or a percussion cap, it was futile to attempt any form of automatic feed and firing.

By the time Maxim had begun his studies the metallic cartridge had arrived, although it was a long way from perfection. By making a cloth belt with loops to hold the individual cartridges, Maxim was able to develop a weapon which would continue to fire, propelled by the force of its own recoil, feeding itself with cartridges, for as long as required. In his first model, it is interesting to note, he used air to cool the barrel. He soon changed this, developing the familiar water-jacket which surrounded the barrel and through which water could be circulated to absorb barrel heat. It is worth bearing in mind that of the energy produced by an exploding cartridge, only about 25% is expended in driving the bullet out of the muzzle; of the remainder, over half is muzzle blast and just under half is heat. A machine

Above **French troops firing a Hotchkiss 8mm machine gun.**

Right **French officers being instructed in the details of a captured German Maxim '08 machine gun. The instructor has opened the receiver of the gun and holds the firing lock in his right hand.**

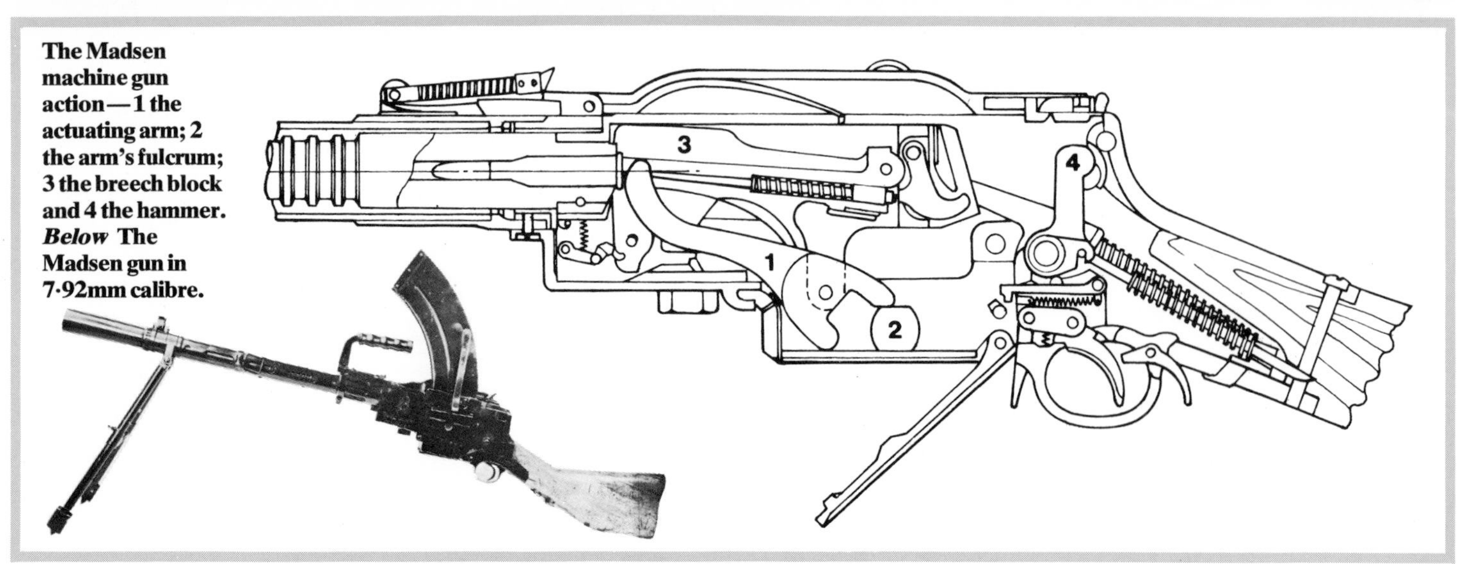

The Madsen machine gun action—1 the actuating arm; 2 the arm's fulcrum; 3 the breech block and 4 the hammer. *Below* The Madsen gun in 7·92mm calibre.

Left **Hiram Maxim, with his machine gun.**
Below **Training aerial gunners during the First World War by firing Lewis guns from trolleys.**
Right **A Vickers 'Gunbus' of the Royal Flying Corps, well-provided with Lewis guns.**

gun firing at 1000 rounds a minute generates about 200 horsepower. The Maxim gun would begin to boil the water in the jacket after about two minutes sustained firing.

Other water-cooled guns followed the Maxim, reflecting the current tactical views; the machine gun was a 'weapon of position' useful for beating off attacks from a prepared defensive post, and in this role it came to dominate the battlefield during the First World War. But that war also brought out the requirement for a light machine gun which could be carried by one man, and this class of weapon came into prominence in the post-war years as the Bren, Chatellerault and Vickers-Berthier (among many others) entered service. Portability argued against carrying gallons of water about, so air-cooling became the accepted method, with the additional feature of rapidly removable barrels, so that after sustained firing had heated the barrel, it could be quickly changed for a cool one and allowed to cool down.

During the Second World War the German Army introduced the concept of the 'general purpose machine gun', an air-cooled weapon which was all things to all men. It could be put on a tripod and used (with several spare barrels) for sustained fire, being belt fed.

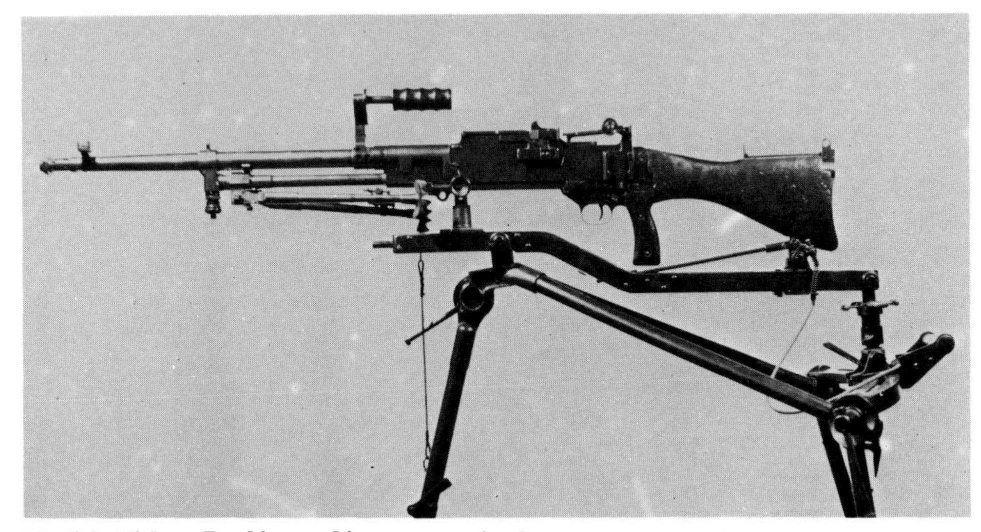

The light Vickers-Berthier machine gun on a tripod.

AUTOMATIC PISTOLS

WHEN MAXIM DEMONSTRATED the ability to use the weapon's own recoil to actuate automatic action, it was an invitation for someone to try and condense the idea into a pistol. The difficulties were enormous, due to the small scale of the weapon and the consequently small size and strength of the component parts and also due to the difficulty (at that time) of producing reliable and consistent ammunition in pistol calibres. A difference in pressure or velocity from shot to shot in a revolver was of little concern to the action of the weapon, but inconsistent ammunition in an automatic pistol gave rise to erratic functioning.

The first automatic pistols designs involved tapping gas from the barrel to drive a piston back and thus cock a revolver hammer. Since the hammer controlled cylinder revolution, it can be seen that such a mechanism would re-cock the revolver and advance the cylinder after each shot. Weapons in this style were developed by Paulson in England (1885) and Orbea in Spain (1863) but were never put on the market. One important feature which both these inventors incorporated in their designs was a 'disconnector', a linkage which automatically disconnects the trigger from the rest of the firing mechanism after each shot and only re-connects them after the firer has consciously released the trigger and taken a fresh grip. Without a disconnector, the guns would have been truly automatic; they would have discharged all their chambers at high speed before the astonished firer had time to realise what was happening and release his grip on the trigger. And since this has applied to pistols ever since, it should be stressed that over 95% of the pistols we call 'automatic' should more properly be called 'self-loading'. The remaining 5% can be switched from the usual self-loading mode of operation so as to disconnect the disconnector and turn the pistol into a genuine automatic which will empty itself in seconds when the trigger is pressed, functioning as a sort of submachine gun. But fortunately these are extremely uncommon because for the most part they are grossly inefficient.

The revolver did not lend itself easily to being converted to an automatic pistol (though it was eventually done with some success in the Webley-Fosbery) and in the 1880s a number of inventors occupied their time in developing a new type of weapon, the 'mechanical repeater'. In almost every case, these used a bolt action, similar to that which had recently become popular in military rifles, and this bolt was propelled back and forth by a lever operated by the forefinger. The firer placed his finger in a ring at the end of this lever, which appeared where the trigger normally lived, and pushed forward; this opened the bolt. He then pulled back, which drove the bolt forward, chambered a cartridge from a magazine, locked the bolt and, at the last moment, released a firing pin to fire the cartridge. When they were new and clean and oiled, these weapons worked reasonably well, but when they were dirty or dry, they took a great deal of muscle-power in the

Right **The Czechoslovakian vz/38 automatic pistol, adopted by the Czech Army in 1939.**

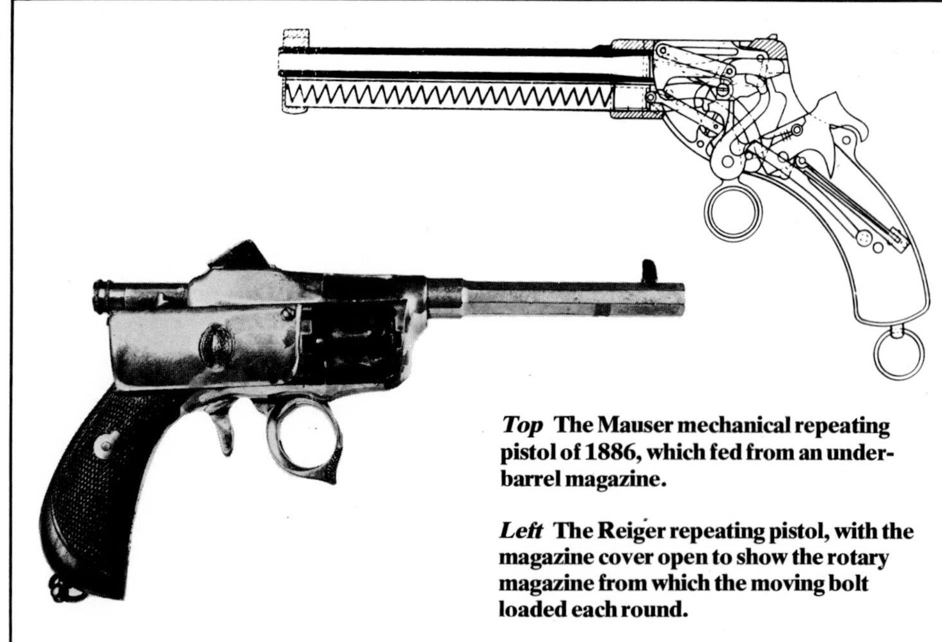

Top **The Mauser mechanical repeating pistol of 1886, which fed from an under-barrel magazine.**

Left **The Reiger repeating pistol, with the magazine cover open to show the rotary magazine from which the moving bolt loaded each round.**

ČESKÁ ZBROJOVKA AKC.SPOL.V PRAZE

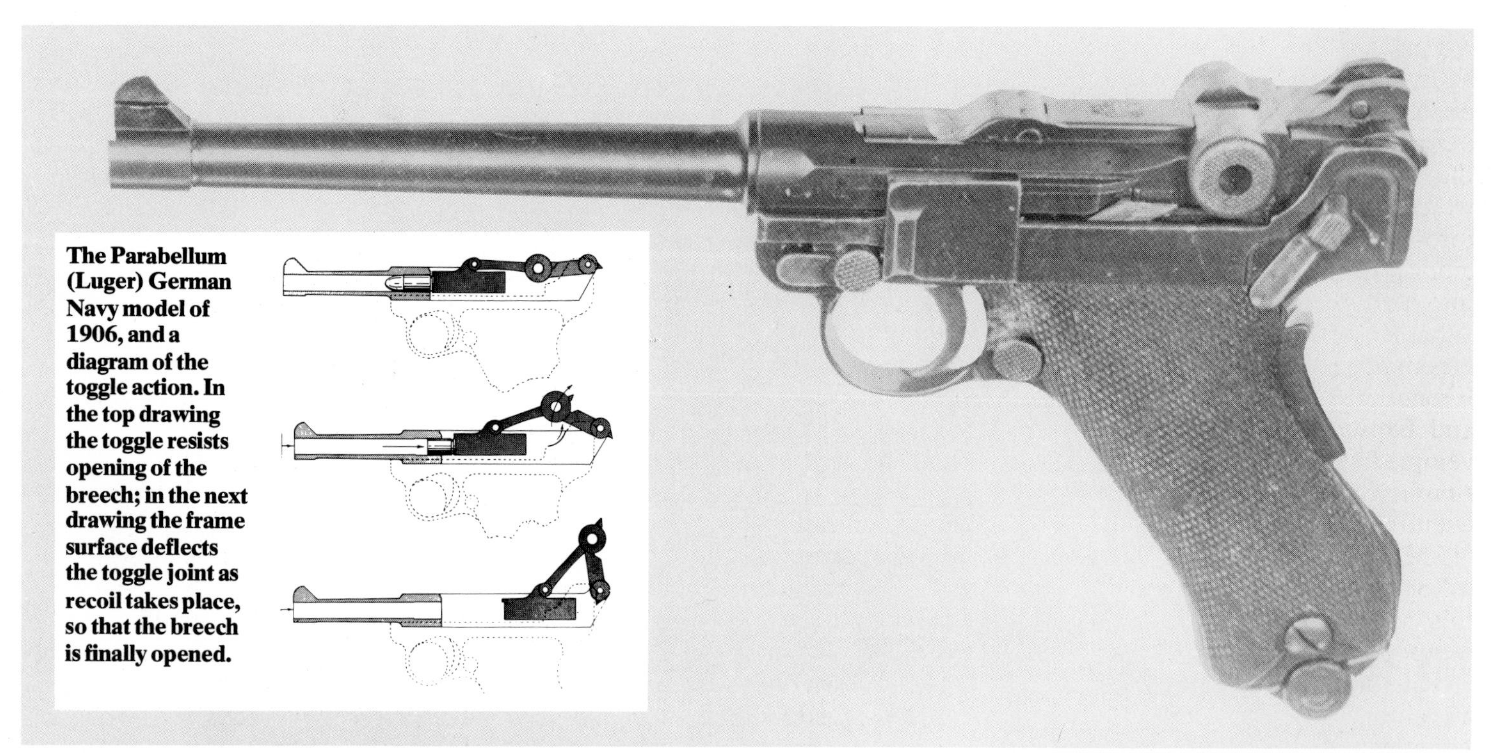

The Parabellum (Luger) German Navy model of 1906, and a diagram of the toggle action. In the top drawing the toggle resists opening of the breech; in the next drawing the frame surface deflects the toggle joint as recoil takes place, so that the breech is finally opened.

forefinger to operate them properly. As a result they did not prosper.

But it was one of these mechanical pistols, modified, which became the first automatic pistol. The Schonberger of 1893 had begun life as the Laumann repeating pistol; it was then altered so that the pressure in the cartridge case forced back the primer cap, so unlocking the breech, after which the remaining pressure in the case blew it back and opened the bolt. This was a remarkable system of operation which has never since been used in a production weapon, principally because it demands the use of special ammunition. And history tells us that guns which demand special ammunition, which cannot be bought over the counter at the local gunsmith, do not prosper. So the Schonberger didn't do very well in the marketplace, and the first pistol to become a commercial success was the Borchardt. This was recoil operated, with the breech locked by a most ingenious toggle system which was probably derived from study of the Maxim machine gun breech lock. After this, the designs came hard on each other's heels; the famous Mauser of 1896, several Bergmann designs, and then the Luger, a refined Borchardt, in 1900.

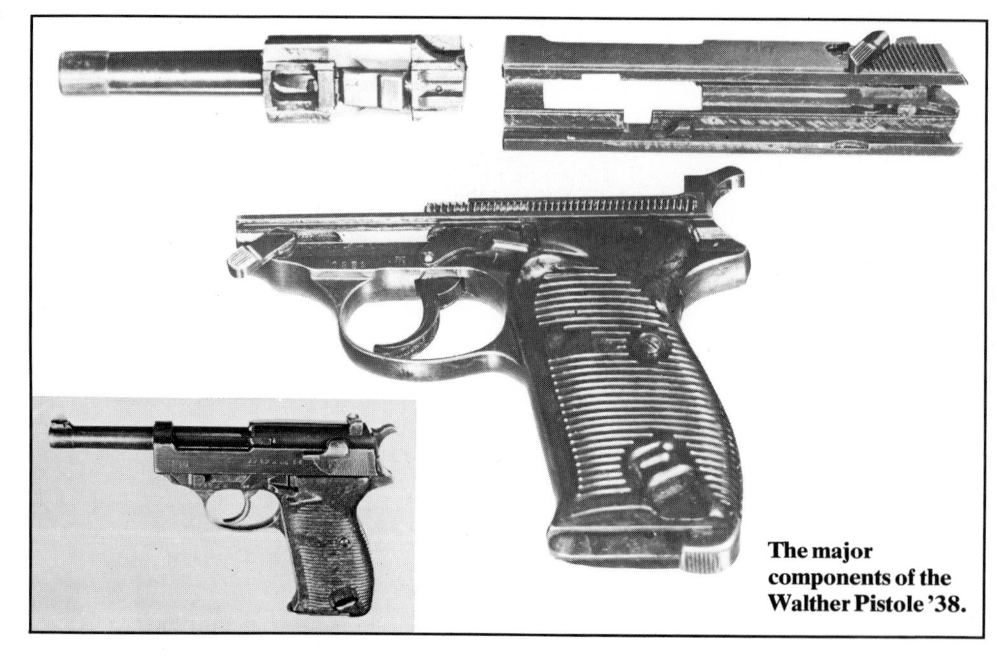

The major components of the Walther Pistole '38.

The United States was strangely deficient of automatic pistol designs at this period—indeed, few good automatic designs have ever come from there—and it was not until John Moses Browning began to study the subject that any progress was made. His first pistols found little interest in

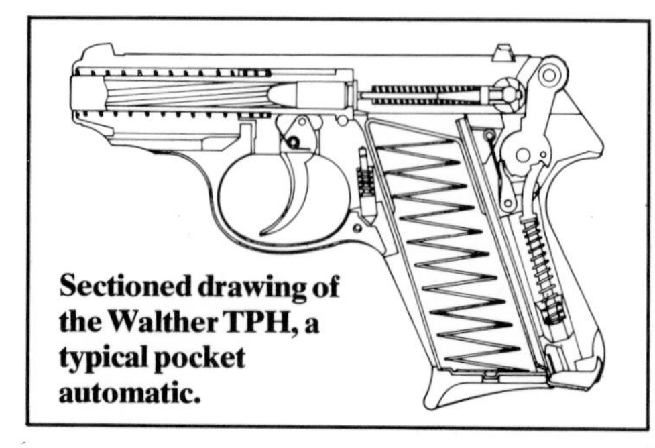

Sectioned drawing of the Walther TPH, a typical pocket automatic.

America, since they were developed as low-powered pocket weapons and no American manufacturer could see a market for then in competition with the multitude of cheap revolvers which were available there. He therefore disposed of his patents in Belgium, where they were transmuted into pistols with enormous success. What America wanted was a powerful automatic in keeping with their preference for large-calibre handguns, and Browning now sat down to develop a locked breech design of classic simplicity and ample strength, which eventually appeared as the Colt ·45 M1911 military pistol, service pistol of the US forces from that day to this and the oldest serving military weapon of any major nation.

This military decision in favour of an automatic pistol finally aroused American interest and a handful of local designs appeared as a result, but, as the manufacturers had feared, competition from inexpensive revolvers was a serious problem, and it was aggravated in the 1920s by an influx of cheap pocket automatics from Germany and Spain, which resulted in the gradual extinction of the American designs other than those of Colt.

Spain had become one of the foremost producers of automatic pistols, having pirated the Browning pocket designs shortly before the First World War. During the war the French and Italian governments, desperate for pistols, placed vast contracts for 7·65mm automatics with Spanish makers, and dozens of small companies sprang up to fill the demand. After the war these companies continued to turn out these 'Eibar' automatics (named from the centre of the Spanish gunmaking trade) and exported them throughout the world at give-away prices. Some of them were good, but far more of them were poorly made of inferior metal, and they gave the Spanish gun trade a bad name which has taken them years to live down. Much of this 'cottage industry' disappeared in the Spanish Civil War.

Major parts of the Steyr M1912 pistol, in which breech locking is done by the rotation of the barrel, controlled by the curved rib on the barrel acting against slots in the pistol frame.

The next major technical step came in 1929 when the Walther company of Germany popularised the double-action lock on automatic pistols. An advantage claimed for the double-action revolver over the automatic was that once loaded, it could be carried safely in an uncocked condition, then drawn and fired by simply pulling through on the trigger. An automatic, on the other hand, had either to be carried cocked, with the safety catch applied, or carried with an empty chamber and hurriedly charged and cocked when the need arose. With the Walther pistol it became possible to load the chamber, lower the hammer in safety, and then, when needed, pull through on the trigger to fire the first shot. The idea had been tried before, but Walther's design was better engineered than its predecessors and became a commercial success. It then went on to gain military acceptance; it was used in the Walther P-38, adopted by the German Army in 1937.

The late 1930s saw a number of new automatic pistols appear, either for the commercial market or for military adoption, and among them were some designs which have survived to the present day. The Walther P-38, above, is still in use by the West German Army. The French designer Charles Petter made some interesting modifications to Browning's locked breech design in a pistol for the French Army. His patents were later bought by a Swiss company and improved to produce the SIG pistols, currently enjoying a high reputation. Browning himself, before his death, made changes in his 1911 design, which later appeared as the 'Browning High Power', and is now probably the world's most widely-sold pistol.

AUTOMATIC RIFLES AND SUBMACHINE GUNS

THE SUBMACHINE GUN bids fair to be the shortest-lived class of military weapon; it was born in the First World War, reached maturity in the Second, and there are indications that within another ten years it will have been discarded from the inventories of every major power.

The submachine gun is properly defined as a short-barrelled automatic weapon which is magazine fed and fires a cartridge normally associated with pistols. It was first developed in this form during 1917–18 for the German Army who wanted a weapon with which to arm their newly-formed 'Storm Troops'. The deadlock on the Western Front had led the Germans to devise a new tactical manoeuvre in which small groups of highly-trained soldiers would filter through the front line under cover of smoke screens and gas bombardments, and for this a weapon of short range but with a high rate of fire and a compact and handy form was wanted. The result was the 'Bergmann Musquete' or 'Kugelspritz' ('bullet-squirter') but the war was over before it had seen sufficient use to justify any tactical lessons being drawn from it.

The victorious Allies were in no doubt; it was not a military weapon, and they forbade it to the German Army, though the German Police forces were permitted to own them, probably due to the civil disturbances which were frequent in the immediate postwar years. It seems that the Army were not particularly distressed, since the military commanders of every nation in those days could see no military niche that the submachine gun could fill; it had been born of unusual tactical conditions which would not occur again, so that was that.

However, the prospect of a compact handful of fire power continued to fascinate some designers, among them the famous General John T. Thompson, who had been working on a small machine gun he called his 'Trench Broom' when the war ended. In an inspired moment he invented the term

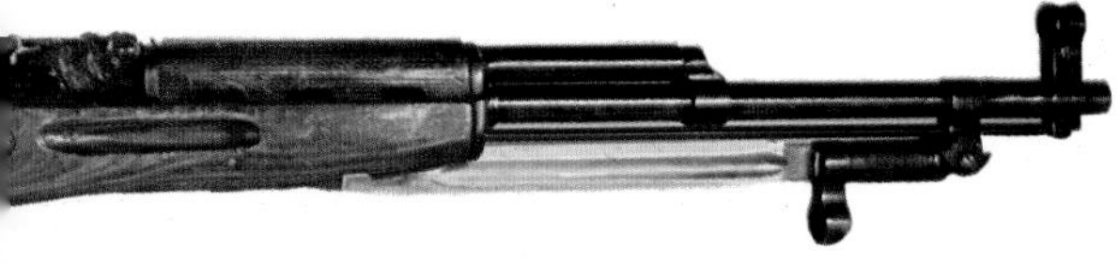

Far left **US Infantryman carrying an Armalite AR15 in Vietnam; the belts are for a different gun.**
Top left **The Simonov SKS 46.**
Left **American troops using the AR15 in 1968.**
Top right **The Australian Owen Gun.**
Right **The Czech Skorpion submachine gun.**

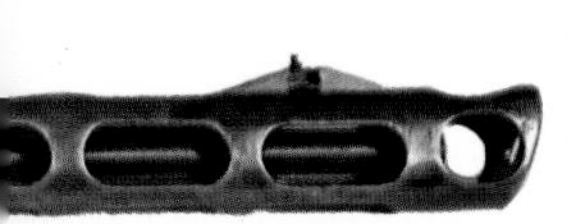

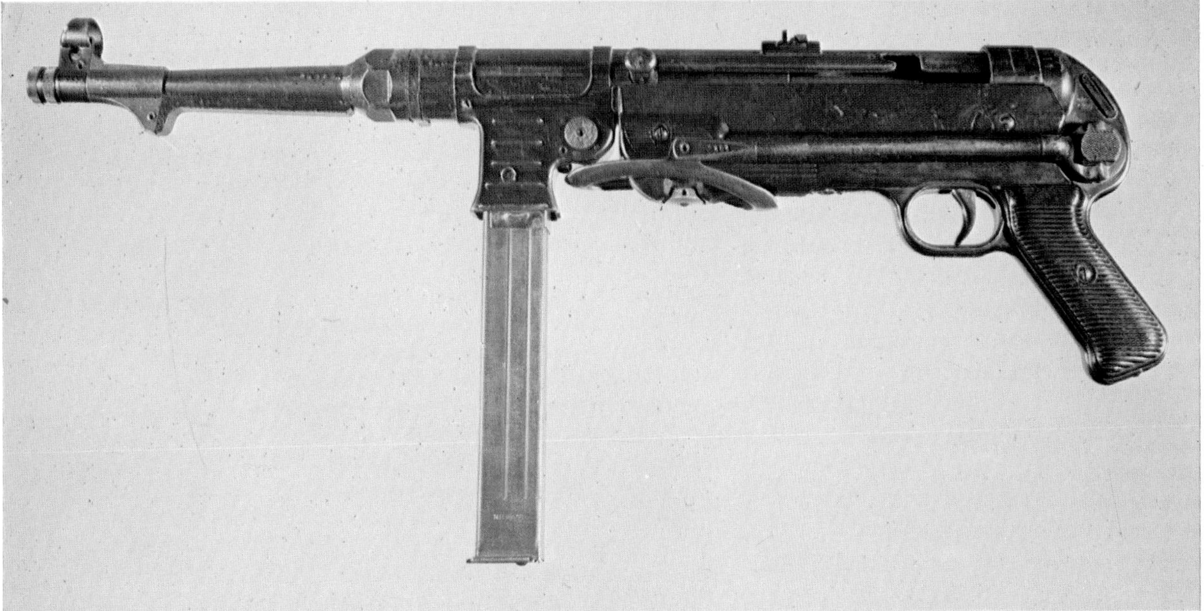

Top **The Bergmann MP18, earliest submachine gun.**
Above **The Soviet PPSh-41 submachine gun of WWII.**
Right **The German MP40.**

'sub machine gun': but his invention, in the hands of the Capone Mob, Machine Gun Kelly, Alvin Karpis and a few of their contemporaries earned it the sobriquet of the 'Tommy Gun', and that is the unfortunate General's memorial.

These American activities gave the submachine gun an unfortunate image, and for too long it was despised as a 'gangster gun' instead of being studied and assessed for a possible role. But the Spanish Civil War saw hundreds of submachine guns put into the field, and it was realised in some quarters that these weapons, simple to teach and use and relatively cheap to make, were the ideal weapon for arming hastily-trained mass armies. Interest in the submachine gun revived once more and in Germany and Russia designs were approved for mass production.

When the Second World War broke out the British Army, who had, in fact, studied the available designs of submachine guns in the 1930s but had been denied finance to equip with them, were forced to buy Thompson guns from the USA. These were expensive, and after the fall of France in 1940 efforts were made to develop a British design. This resulted in the famous Sten Gun, the epitome of cheap and expendable construction in firearms, a simple tube with a bolt working inside it, a short barrel on one end, a steel-tube butt at the other, and a magazine feeding into the side. At the height of wartime production these were being turned out for about £2.50 each, and as well as equipping British troops they were distributed wholesale to resistance groups throughout Occupied Europe.

Russia undoubtedly held the record for volume production, turning out submachine guns by the million and arming whole regiments with nothing else. Moreover, the submachine gun suited the Russian tactical doctrines; it was a weapon of attack, not of defence. The Americans also developed their own cheap expendable gun,

Above **John Garand in his workshop.**

Below **The Garand rifle action. The bolt (1) is driven by a gas piston. The follower (2) forces rounds from the clip (3) into the bolt's path. When the trigger is pressed the hammer (4) strikes the firing pin (5).**

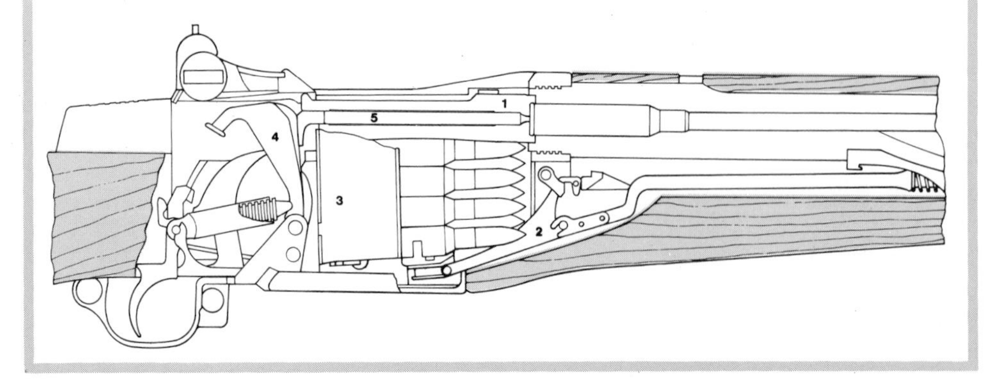

Above **The Sten Gun in its 'Mark 2' version.**
Below **French Maquisard firing his Sten gun, air-dropped by the thousand to resistance groups all over Europe.**

known as the 'grease gun' from its simple cylindrical shape. Strangely, the Japanese, who would have benefited immeasurably in their jungle and Pacific campaigns by having a good submachine gun, ignored the weapon and produced only a small number for use by their airborne troops.

After the war the general quality of guns improved, once the pressure was off, and the move was towards compactness, aided by the development of the 'overhung' or 'telescoping' bolt. In this design the front face of the bolt is hollowed out so that when the bolt is closed much of the mass lies ahead of the chamber mouth and actually surrounds the barrel. This allows the overall length of the gun to be reduced and also makes for a better-balanced weapon and one which can easily be used single-handed.

In the 1960s the small-calibre assault rifle became popular; due to its shorter cartridge this type of weapon was more handy than the 'traditional' rifle firing a full-size round, and many of the designs were capable of automatic fire. The Soviets adopted one of the first assault rifles in the late 1940s and they very quickly realised that it could do almost everything that a submachine gun could. Since it makes logical sense to reduce the number of different weapons in an army, the submachine gun was retired and the Kalashnikov rifle became the standard infantry weapon. As other armies gained experience with assault rifles they agreed with this view. In the United States Army the submachine gun has been relegated to the reserve, and if the British 4·85mm Individual Weapon, currently under evaluation, is adopted, it will replace the Sterling submachine gun as well as the FAL rifle. The submachine gun will have reverted to its 1920s gangster status.

THE FIREARMS OF THE FUTURE

INVITATIONS TO PROPHESY are generally invitations to disaster, but the firearms field is perhaps less liable than most to take flight in unexpected directions. Things have a habit of moving in cycles in the ordnance world; ideas seem to appear before they have the necessary technological backing, fade away, and then reappear with amazing regularity, and it is largely a matter of seeing what went wrong last time in order to be able to guess what will be appearing shortly.

A case in point is the selective-fire automatic pistol. During the early parts of the First World War some experimenters tried taking the disconnector out of an automatic pistol and fitting it with an over-long magazine, the object being a one-hand rapid-fire weapon for early aviators. The result was not very practical, because the light weight of the recoiling parts set up a high rate of fire, and the reciprocating slide or bolt above the firer's wrist caused the muzzle to climb very rapidly into the air so that most of the shots were wasted. In the early 1930s the idea was revived in Spain, this time with the addition of a clip-on wooden butt which, it was hoped, would make the gun more controllable. It didn't.

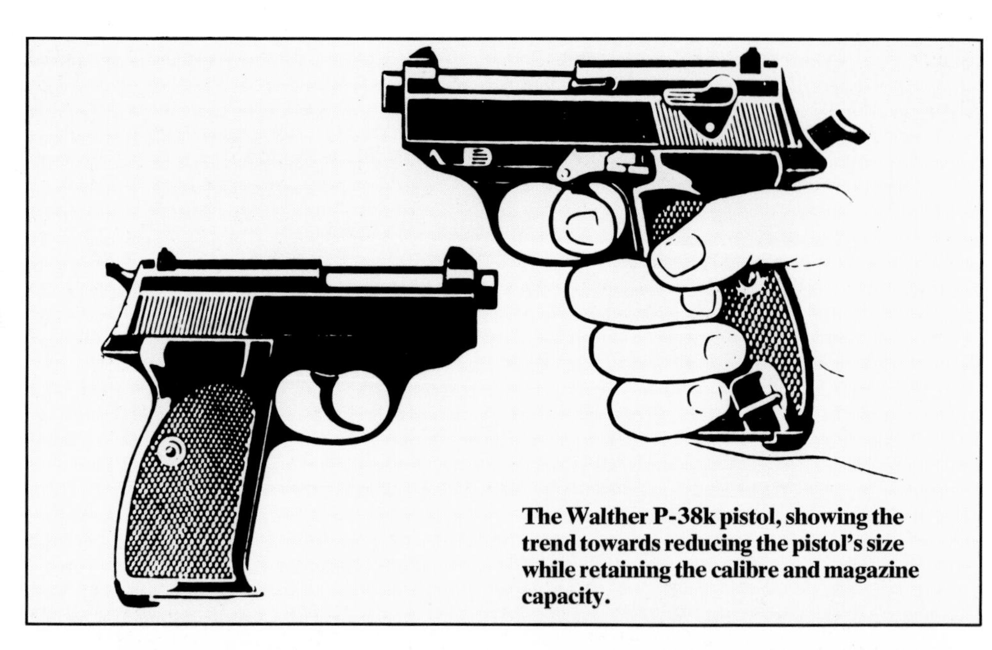

The Walther P-38k pistol, showing the trend towards reducing the pistol's size while retaining the calibre and magazine capacity.

The 9mm 'Mamba', a double-action automatic pistol in stainless steel.

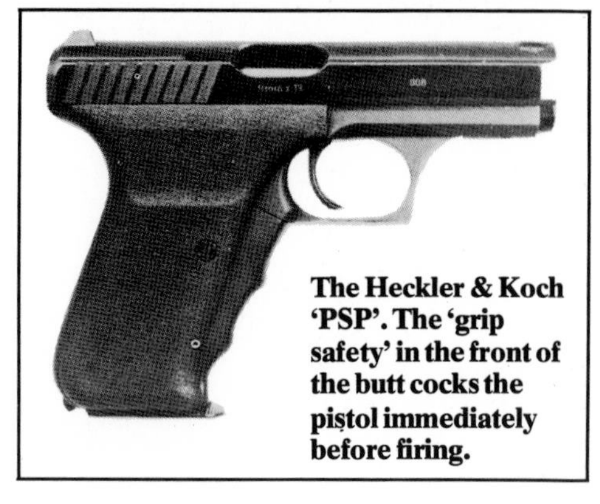

The Heckler & Koch 'PSP'. The 'grip safety' in the front of the butt cocks the pistol immediately before firing.

***Left* The Heckler & Koch VP-70 pistol with butt attachment. This pistol has a 'burst-fire' facility which allows it to function as a submachine gun.**

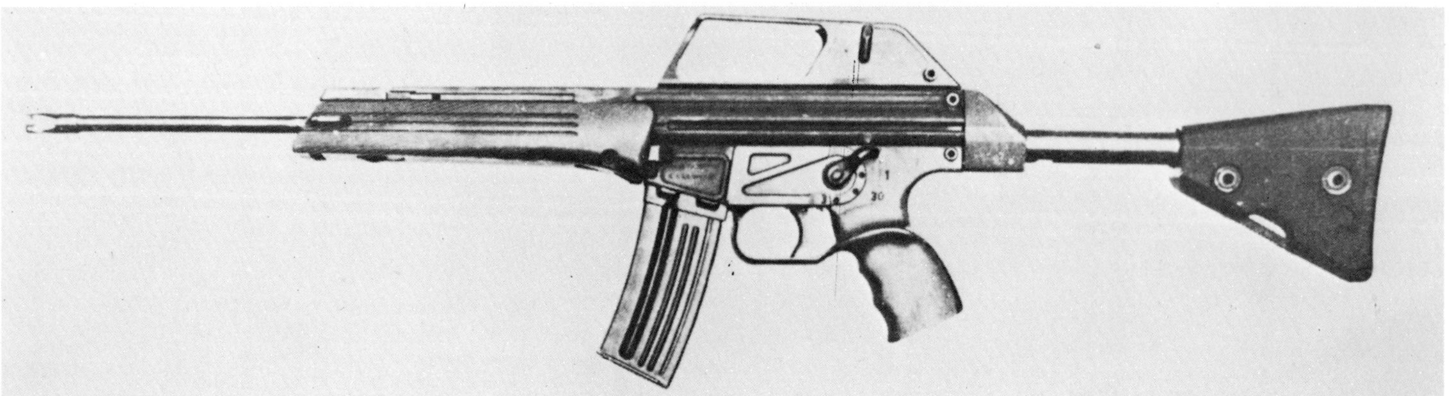

***Below* The Heckler & Koch HK 36 assault rifle, an experimental weapon in 4·5mm calibre.**

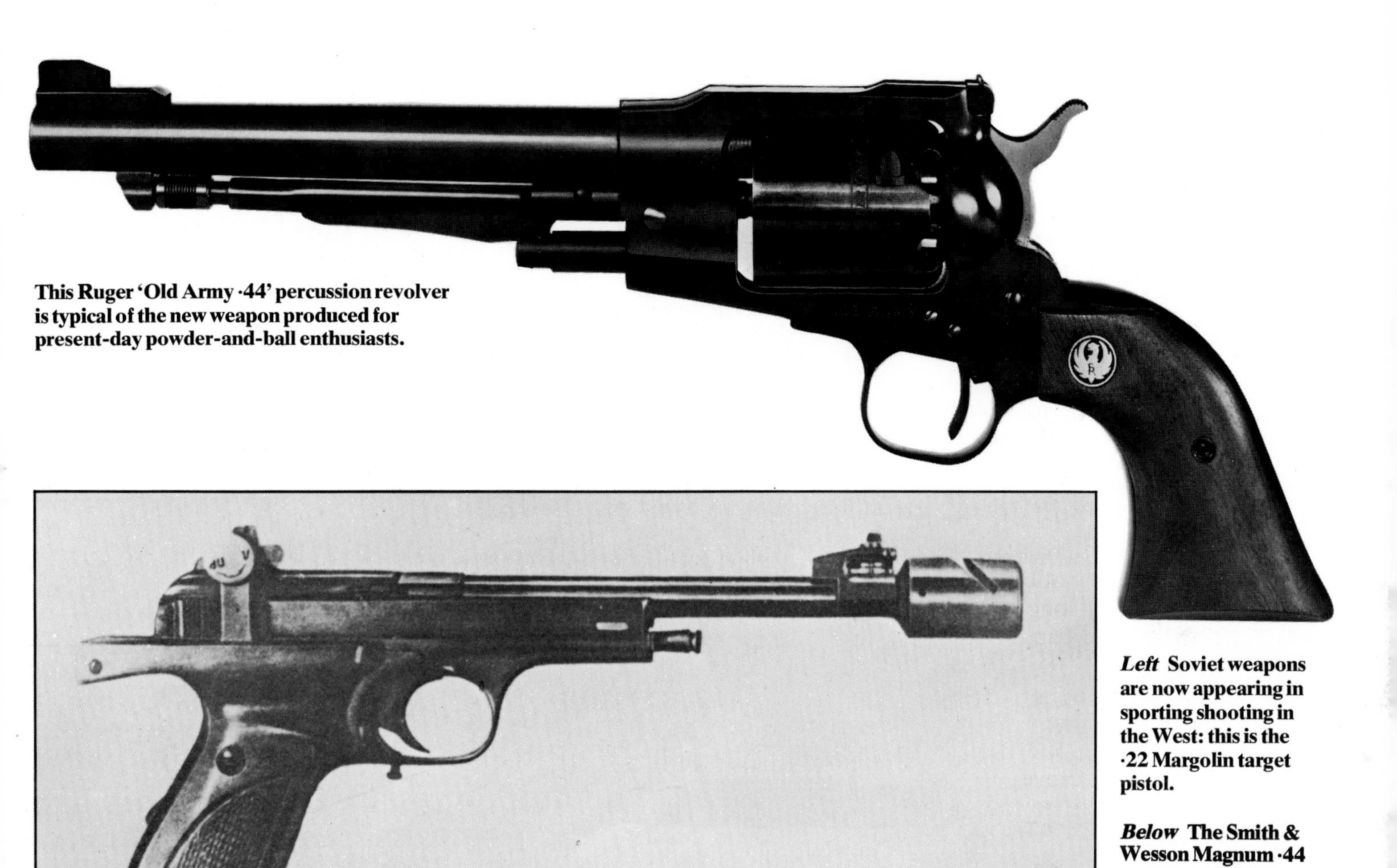

This Ruger 'Old Army ·44' percussion revolver is typical of the new weapon produced for present-day powder-and-ball enthusiasts.

Left **Soviet weapons are now appearing in sporting shooting in the West: this is the ·22 Margolin target pistol.**

Below **The Smith & Wesson Magnum ·44 is typical of the heavy revolvers needed to cater for the current fashion in powerful pistol cartridges.**

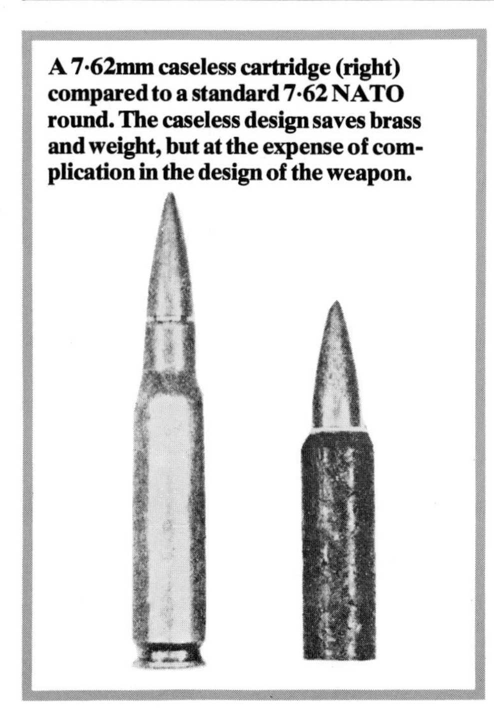

A 7·62mm caseless cartridge (right) compared to a standard 7·62 NATO round. The caseless design saves brass and weight, but at the expense of complication in the design of the weapon.

The 'machine pistol' appeared again in the 1950s when the Russian Army embraced the 'Stetchkin', but that soon faded away. Now the Heckler & Koch company of Germany have revived the idea but with a technical refinement: a controller which restricts a burst of fire to only three rounds every time the trigger is pressed. This prevents excessive rise of the muzzle and allows the firer to get back on target quickly for another burst; it also conserves ammunition. Reception of the idea seems to be mixed at the moment, and only time will tell whether the machine pistol is in for a new lease of life or is merely making one of its many temporary comebacks.

Military rifles can be expected to shrink both in calibre and in overall size as cartridges become smaller. This gradual move to 'miniature' ammunition has been gathering speed since the Germans introduced their 7·92mm 'Kurz' cartridge in 1943. Briefly, the arguments are that a large cartridge is superfluous since the soldier rarely shoots at anything more than 350–400 yards away; a short cartridge and small bullet will give satisfactory results at that range and will allow a smaller and lighter rifle to be used. The stumbling block was the demand that the bullet still had to do some worthwhile damage, and this appeared to demand the retention of a substantial calibre. The introduction of the 5·56mm (·223) cartridge in the 1950s, though, showed that small calibres could incapacitate just as effectively as large ones, provided the bullet was carefully matched to the weapon. With the 5·56mm bullet it was found that the twist of rifling and the amount of spin imparted to the bullet was critical; the bullet was spun so as to be just stable in flight, but it lost stability instantly when it encountered anything substantial. As a result, it toppled, gave up its energy rapidly, and dealt out severe wounds. From this starting point ballisticians began working downward, and at present calibres as small as 4mm (0·157 inch) are being evaluated.

Similar studies have been applied to hunting ammunition, since much the same criteria appear to apply to shooting game as to shooting men, and if small calibres work for military rifles they should also work for hunting rifles. However, there is rather more to this than simple wound ballistics and calculations based on 'stopping power' might indicate. The man who designs the ammunition can never be sure what the man who buys it intends to shoot, and animals are vastly different from specie to specie; the bullet which will stop a deer may not necessarily stop a bison, and a great deal of the effectiveness of hunting cartridges is bound up with the degree of expertise of the hunter. Nevertheless, working on the assumption that a man willing to try out new ammunition must have some idea of what he is up to, new calibre and bullet weights are being introduced for those willing to try them. There was a rash of ·17 inch cartridges some fifteen to twenty years ago, most of which failed to survive; some of the new offerings are in this calibre area and it remains to be seen whether they will do any better. In our view these new calibres may well fill the bill for some particular applications and with some particular hunters, but as a general rule it is unlikely that they will make much impression on the popularity of the long-established hunting cartridges.

One of the more recent firearms phenomena is the revival of 'black powder shooting' using replicas of muzzle loading flintlock and percussion weapons. The reasons for this are extremely diverse, ranging from the simple enjoyment of an uncomplicated artifact, by means of the pleasure gained from shooting a home-made (or at least home-finished) gun, to the somewhat studied postures of the ecological brigade who feel that hunting with more primitive weapons gives the animal a better chance of survival. Whatever the reason, its popularity is attested to by the increasing number of guns on the market and clubs being formed to shoot them, and since this form of shooting appears cheaper than some others, it should continue to prosper.

Pistol design scarcely moves these days, when just about every feasible way of making a pistol has been explored. The tendency is towards heavier calibres with more powerful loading—the Magnum cartridges—in order to produce either long-range accuracy or short-range destructive power. Another present-day field of endeavour is the gradual reduction in size of the pistol without reducing the calibre. The Colt ·45 M1911 automatic is 8½ inches long and weighs 40 ounces, and it was always considered to be a difficult gun to master due to the powerful cartridge and heavy recoil. Yet a recently announced ·45 auto pistol, the Thomas, is 6½ inches long and weighs 32 ounces, while the Spanish 'Star PD ·45' is 7½ inches long and weighs an incredible 24 ounces. This tendency probably accounts for the current fashion for holding pistols with two hands, even though the makers are still putting only one handle on them.

Firearms have come a long way in the past 650 years: it would be tempting to think that they have reached the limit of their development, since it seems difficult to visualise any major innovation. But they probably thought the same thing when the flintlock was perfected. Leaving aside the emotive and psychological questions which firearms frequently invoke, it has to be admitted that the firearm is a considerable engineering feat—just think for a moment of what goes on inside a machine gun a thousand times a minute—and there is never likely to be a shortage of individuals who are convinced that they have discovered a better way of solving the basic mechanical problems. I am prepared to make a small wager that within the next ten years, something will have come along to surprise us all.